GLOOSKAP'S COUNTRY
AND OTHER INDIAN TALES

OXFORD UNIVERSITY PRES

GLOOSKAP'S COUNTRY
AND OTHER INDIAN TALES

BY

CYRUS MACMILLAN

ILLUSTRATED BY

JOHN A. HALL

TORONTO   NEW YORK   1956

The stories in this collection were first published
by John Lane, The Bodley Head, Limited in
Canadian Wonder Tales (1918) and
Canadian Fairy Tales (1922).

Printed in Canada
by
MARACLE PRESS LIMITED

Contents

Glooskap's Country

In far-back times many centuries before the white men came from Europe to live in the New World, Eastern Canada was inhabited by Indians. They were a mighty race, great in size and strong in battle. Their descendants live in certain of these parts still, dwelling in settlements of their own apart from the white folk. You may still see them in their strange tents or wigwams, making arrows and baskets and garden-seats. Some of them are still fleet of foot and can run many miles without tiring. But their real greatness has long since gone. They have grown smaller in size, and they are no longer powerful as in the old days. In early times they were called the Children of Light, for of all the people in America they dwelt nearest to the sunrise. Their great lord and creator was Glooskap. Where he was himself born, and when, no man knows. From the place of his birth he sailed across the sea in a great stone canoe to the part of America nearest to the rising sun. He landed on the eastern shores of

Canada. Far out he anchored his canoe, and it was so large that it became an island, and great trees grew upon it. When he needed it, it was always ready to do his bidding, but it always became an island when it was not in use. On the shore of the Atlantic Ocean, Glooskap dwelt many years—ages and ages—until one day he sailed away to the hunting grounds of his fathers far over the sea.

About Glooskap's work many strange tales are told. From his birth and throughout his long life his deeds were very wonderful. He was one of twin brothers, the other being Wolf the son of Wickedness. Glooskap was the son of Goodness. Their mother died at their birth and the two children were left alone. Both had magic power which could keep them from harm, and death could not come to them except in one way. Glooskap could be killed only by a flowering rush, and Wolf only by a fern root; and each alone knew the secret of his own death.

Now it was known before Glooskap's birth that he should become the Lord of the Land of the Rising Sun in Canada. But Beaver and Squirrel, who were great in those days—and even before his coming—were jealous of his power when he arrived, for they themselves wished to rule the land. They tempted Wolf to kill his brother and he, being the son of Wickedness, would have been glad of the chance, but he did not know the secret of his brother's death. One night of bright starlight, Beaver, hiding stealthily among the trees as was his custom, heard Glooskap boasting to the stars about his charmed life; he could trust the stars, and he told them that he could be killed only by means of a flowering rush. Then Beaver hurried away to Wolf. He told him that he knew the secret of Glooskap's death and that he would tell it if Wolf would give him what he wished. To this Wolf agreed, and Beaver told him what he had heard Glooskap say to the stars. 'What do you want in return for the secret?' asked Wolf. 'Wings like a pigeon,' answered Beaver. But Wolf said: 'You have a tail like a file. What could you do with wings like a pigeon?' And he laughed at him scornfully and would not grant him his wish as he had promised. Thereupon Beaver was very cross and resolved to have vengeance on Wolf. He went quickly to Glooskap and told him that Wolf knew the secret of his death and that he had better be on his guard.

The next night Glooskap hid himself among the trees near to Wolf's tent. He heard Wolf boasting to the stars about his charmed life and telling them the secret of his death—that he could be killed only by a fern root. And Glooskap, fearing for his own life, for he had no faith in the love of Wolf the son of Wickedness, at once slew his brother with a fern root. Then he changed him into a mountain, where he sleeps to this day like a huge hill.

Glooskap then ruled the country alone. But soon he grew lonely without companions and he decided to people his land. He first made the Fairies and the Elves, and sent them to dwell in the meadows and tiny streams and among the hills and caves. Then he took his bow and arrows, and for many days he shot at the ash trees in the forest. And out of the bark of the trees at which he shot there came first men whom he called Indians, the Children of Light. Then came the animals—all that had not before lived in his land—and the birds of the air and the fish of the sea, and he gave them each a name. At first all the animals were very large, so large that the head of the deer could touch the tops of the tallest pines. Even Squirrel could tear down the largest trees in the forest. One day Glooskap called all the animals to him to learn if they were friendly to his people. And he said to Bear: 'What would you do if you should meet a man?' And Bear answered: 'I should eat him up.' And Glooskap sent Bear away to the Northland, far from the dwellings of men, to live on fish from the frozen sea. And he said to Squirrel: 'What would you do if you should meet a man?' And squirrel answered: 'I should tear down trees on his head.' And Glooskap, fearing for his men because of the strength of the animals, decided to make the animals smaller. So he took Squirrel and smoothed his back with his hand for a whole day until he became very small, as he is now, and he made him carry his tail on his back that he might thereby use up some of his strength; but Squirrel still scratches as in the old days.

Glooskap made all the animals smaller and weaker than they were when they were first created. He gave his people power over them so that the greatest and strongest of all his creatures was man. The animals became his friends and the friends of his people; they could talk like men and they often spoke to them, and they were eager to obey Glooskap and to help him in his work. Two great wolves became his dogs; he could change their size and make them kind or cruel as he willed. They guarded his tent by day and night and always followed him about, even swimming behind him when he went far away over the sea. The loons of the beach became his messengers, and one of them—old Tatler—became his chief tale-bearer. They always brought him news from other lands over the water and they also kept him well informed

about the deeds of his own people, telling him who were good and who were evil. Fox, too, brought tales from places deep in the forest, and was one of his most trusted friends. The rabbits became the guides of men; one of them—old Bunny—was his scout of the woods, and those who followed him never lost their way. The partridge built boats for men and animals until, because of the bird's stupidity, Glooskap took away his power. The whale became his carrier, and old Blob the Whale came quickly to his call and carried him on her back when he wished to go far over the sea. The Great Eagle made the winds for him. When she moved her wings, the winds blew; she could make them great or gentle as Glooskap commanded, and when Glooskap tied her wings, the winds were still. Each animal and bird had special work to do.

Glooskap's only enemies were Beaver and Badger and Bull Frog. These always plotted against him and tried to destroy his power by stirring up strife among his people. At last he could be patient with them no longer, and he resolved to drive Beaver away. One day when Beaver watched him from a distance, Glooskap scooped up great handfuls of earth and stones and threw them in anger at his enemy, and Beaver, in great fear because of Glooskap's great power, fled far away. The earth that Glooskap threw fell into the ocean and became islands. The spot from which Glooskap had taken the earth became a beautiful bay. To the shores of this bay Glooskap moved his tent and lived there until he left the earth. When Beaver went away, he built a dam from a high place on the south to the shore on the north, and he thought to live there in comfort. But the dam caused the high tides of the sea to overflow the valley, and it was a source of trouble and fear to the people who lived near it. Thereupon Glooskap in anger one day broke the dam and pushed part of it out into the sea. The broken part which he moved out became a cape stretching into the ocean, and there you may see it to this day. Then Beaver, knowing that Glooskap was more powerful than he, troubled him openly no more, but frequently by stealth he tried to do him harm.

When Bull Frog was first created, he was given power over all the fresh-water streams in the land. He dwelt in the stream from which Glooskap's people took water for their use—for drinking and cooking. But he too proved false to Glooskap, and grew vain of his own great power. Once, that he might show his skill and win a great reputation among men, he dried up the water in the stream until only the mud remained. The people thirsted without fresh water and were distressed, and at last they complained to Glooskap.

Glooskap told them not to worry, for he would soon set things right. That he might make sure of Bull Frog's treachery, he went himself to the bank of the stream and there he asked a boy to bring him water to drink. The boy searched for water for a whole day while Glooskap sat on a log and silently smoked his pipe. At last the boy came back bringing only a small cup, no larger than a thimble, filled with dirty water, and said it was all the water he could get.

Glooskap knew then that his people had told him the truth about Bull Frog's wickedness. In great anger he went himself to the mud where Bull Frog dwelt and asked for water. But Bull Frog stubbornly refused to let the water come forth. Then Glooskap grasped Bull Frog with a mighty grip and squeezed him tight until he crumpled his back and made him soft. With a great force he hurled him far out into the mud, and said: 'Henceforth you shall live in dirty water; and you shall always croak with a dry throat as a punishment for your sins.' Then with his own magic power he brought forth water so that the stream flowed again, and the people all rejoiced. He promised that never again should any creature have power to dry up the streams. And since that time Bull Frog has lived in muddy pools; he still croaks, for his throat is always dry, and to this day his back is wrinkled and crumpled and bears the marks of Glooskap's mighty fingers. And since that day the supply of clear water has never failed in the country, and the streams have never dried up.

Glooskap was always kind to his people. He taught the men how to hunt and how to build huts and canoes. He taught them what plants were good to eat, and he told them the names of all the stars. But he did not dwell among his men. He dwelt apart from them in a great tent, but when they sought him they always found him. He never married as they did. There dwelt with him as his housekeeper a very wise old woman; her name was Dame Bear, but Glooskap called her always 'Grandmother'. With him too there lived a little boy whom Glooskap always called 'Little Brother'. And Glooskap gave him a magic root from the forest by the use of which he could change his shape into various forms. Whether or not Dame Bear was really his grandmother or the little boy his brother, no man knows. But both lived with him until his death.

Glooskap and Dame Bear and the little boy lived together for many ages. Glooskap had a magic belt which gave him power over sickness and hunger and danger and death. And anyone on whom it was placed was given the same strange power. And while Glooskap was with them, his people lived very happily. They never wanted for food or clothing. For Glooskap was kind to his people and wished them to be contented and at peace.

How Summer Came to Canada

Once during Glooskap's lifetime and reign in Canada it grew very cold. Everywhere there was snow and ice, and in all the land there was not a flower nor a leaf left alive. The fires that the Indians built could not bring warmth. The food supply was slowly eaten up, and the people were unable to grow more corn because of the hard frozen ground. Great numbers of men and women and children died daily from cold and hunger, and it seemed as if the whole land must soon perish.

Over the extreme cold Glooskap had no power. He tried all his magic, but it was of no avail. For the cold was caused by a powerful giant who came into the land from the far north, bringing Famine and Death as his helpers. Even with his breath he could blight and wither the trees so that they brought forth no leaves nor fruit; and he could destroy the corn and kill man and beast. The giant's name was Winter. He was very old and very strong, and he had ruled in the far north long before the coming of man. Glooskap, being brave and wishing to help his people in their need, went alone to the giant's tent to try to coax or bribe or force him to go away. But even he, with all his magic power, at once fell in love with the giant's home; for in the sunlight it sparkled like crystal and was of many wonderful colours, but in the night under the moonlight it was spotlessly white. From the tent, when Glooskap looked out, the face of the earth was beautiful. The trees had a covering of snow that gave them strange fantastic shapes. The sky was filled by night with flashing quivering lights, and even the stars had a new brightness. The forest, too, was full of mysterious noises. Glooskap soon forgot his people amid his new surroundings. The giant told him tales of olden times when all the land was silent and white and beautiful like his sparkling tent. After a time the giant used his charm of slumber and inaction until Glooskap fell asleep, for the charm was the charm of the Frost. For six months he slept like a bear. Then he awoke, for he was very strong and Winter could not kill him even in his sleep. But when he arose he was hungry and very tired.

One day soon after he awoke, his tale-bearer, Tatler the Loon, brought him good news. He told of a wonderful Southland, far away, where it was always warm, and where lived a Queen who could easily overcome the giant; indeed, she was the only one on earth whose power the giant feared. Loon described carefully the road to the new country. Glooskap, to save his people from Winter and Famine and Death, decided to go to the Southland and find the Queen. So he went to the sea, miles away, and sang the magic song that the whales obeyed. His old friend Blob the Whale came quickly to his call and, get-

ting on her back, he sailed away. Now the whale always had a strange law for travellers. She said to Glooskap: 'You must shut your eyes tight while I carry you; to open them is dangerous, for if you do, I will surely go aground on a reef or a sand-bar and cannot get off, and you may then be drowned.' And Glooskap promised to keep his eyes shut.

Many days the whale swam, and each day the water grew warmer, and the air grew gentler and sweeter, for it came from spicy shores; and the smells were no longer those of the salt sea, but of fruits and flowers and pines. Soon they saw in the sky by night the Southern Cross. They found, too, that they were no longer in the deep sea, but in shallow water flowing warm over yellow sands, and that land lay not far ahead. Blob the Whale now swam more cautiously.

Down in the sand the clams were singing a song of warning, telling travellers in these strange waters of the treacherous sand-bar beneath. 'Oh, big whale,' they said, 'keep out to sea, for the water here is shallow and you shall come to grief if you keep on to shore.' But the whale did not understand the language of the little clams, and she said to Glooskap, who understood: 'What do they sing?' But Glooskap, wishing to land at once, answered: 'They tell you to hurry, for a storm is coming—to hurry along as fast as you can.' Then the whale hurried until she was soon close to the land. Glooskap, wishing the whale to go aground so that he could more easily walk ashore, opened his left eye and peeped, which was contrary to the whale's laws. And at once the whale stuck hard and fast on the beach, so that Glooskap, springing from her head, walked ashore on dry land. The whale, thinking that she could never get off, was very angry, and sang a song of lament and blame. But Glooskap put one end of his strong bow against the whale's jaw and, taking the other end in his hands, he placed his feet against the high bank, and with a mighty push he sent Old Blob again into the deep water. Then, to keep the whale's friendship, he threw her an old pipe and a bag of Indian tobacco leaves—for Glooskap was a great smoker—and the whale, greatly pleased with the gift, lighted the pipe and, smoking it, swam far out to sea. Glooskap watched her disappear from view until he could see only clouds of her smoke against the sky. And to this day the whale has Glooskap's old pipe, and sailors often see her rise to the surface to smoke it in peace and to blow rings of tobacco smoke into the air.

When the whale had gone, Glooskap walked with great strides far inland. Soon he found the way of which Loon had told him. It was the Rainbow Road that led to the Wilderness of Flowers. It lay through the land of the Sunrise, beautiful and fresh in the morning light. On each side were sweet magnolias and palms, and all kinds of

trees and flowers. The grass was soft and velvety, for by
night the dew was always on it; and snow and hail were
unknown and winds never blew coldly, for here the
charm of the frost had no power.

Glooskap went quickly along the flower-lined Rainbow
Road until he came to an orange grove where the air was
sweet with the scent of blossoms. Soon he heard sounds of
music. He peered through the trees and saw that the
sounds came from an open space not far ahead where the
grass was soft and where tiny streams were flowing and
making melody. It was lilac-time in the land, and around
the open space all kinds of flowers in the world were
blooming. On the trees numberless birds were singing—
birds of wonderfully coloured feathers such as Glooskap
had never heard or seen before. He knew that he had
reached at last the Wilderness of Flowers of which old
Tatler the Loon had spoken. He drew deep breaths of
honeysuckle and heliotrope and countless other flowers
until he soon grew strong again after his long voyage.

Then he crept close to the edge of the open space and
looked in from behind the trees. On the flower-covered
grass within, many fair maidens were singing and dancing, holding in their hands chains of blossoms like children in a Maypole game. In the centre of the group was
one fairer than all the others—the most beautiful creature he had ever seen, her long brown hair crowned with
flowers and her arms filled with blossoms. For some time
Glooskap gazed in silence, for he was too surprised to
move or to utter speech. Then he saw at his side an old
woman—wrinkled and faded, but still beautiful—like
himself watching the dance. He found his voice and
asked: 'Who are those maidens in the Wilderness of

Flowers?' And the old woman answered: 'The maiden in the centre of the group is the Fairy Queen; her name is Summer. She is the daughter of the rosy Dawn—the most beautiful ever born. The maidens dancing with her are her children, the Fairies of Light and Sunshine and Flowers.'

Glooskap knew that here at last was the Queen who by her charms could melt old Winter's heart and force him to go away, for she was very beautiful and good. With his magic song he lured her from her children into the dark forest; there he seized her and held her fast by a crafty trick. Then, with her as a companion, he began his long return journey north by land. That he might know the way back to the Wilderness of Flowers, he cut a large moose hide, which he always carried, into a long slender cord, and as he ran north with Summer, he let the cord unwind behind him, for he had no time to mark the trail in the usual way. When they had gone, Summer's children mourned greatly for their Queen. For weeks the tears ran down their cheeks like rain on all the land, and for a long time, old Dawn, the Queen's mother, covered herself with dark mourning clouds and refused to be bright.

After many days, still holding Summer in his bosom—for she loved him because of his magic power—Glooskap reached the Northland. He found none of his people, for they were all asleep under the giant's power, and the whole country was cold and lonely. At last he came to the home of old Winter. The giant welcomed him and the beautiful girl, for he hoped to freeze them both and keep them with him always. For some time they talked together in the tent, but, although he tried hard, the

giant was unable to put them to sleep. Soon old Winter
felt that his power had vanished and that the charm of
the Frost was broken. Large drops of sweat ran down his
face; then his tent slowly disappeared and he was left
homeless. Summer used her strange power until every-
thing that Winter had put to sleep awoke again. Buds
came again upon the trees; the snow ran down the rivers
carrying away the dead leaves; and the grass and the
corn sprang up with new life. And old Winter, being
sorrowful, wept, for he knew that his reign was ended,
and his tears were like cold rain.

Summer, the Queen, seeing him mourn and wishing to

stop his tears, said: 'I have proved that I am more powerful than you; I give you now all the country to the far north for your own, and there I shall never disturb you. You may come back to Glooskap's country six months of every year and reign as of old, but you will be less severe; during the other six months, I myself will come from the Southland and rule the land.'

Old Winter could do nothing but accept this offer gracefully, for he feared that if he did not he would melt entirely away. So he built a new home farther north, and there he reigns without interruption. In the late autumn he comes back to Glooskap's country and reigns for six months, but his rule is softer than in olden times. And when he comes, Summer, following Glooskap's moosehide cord, runs home with her birds to the Wilderness of Flowers. But at the end of six months she always comes back to drive old Winter away to his own land, to awaken the northern world, and to bring it the joys that only she, the Queen, can give. And so in Glooskap's old country, Winter and Summer, the hoary old giant and the beautiful Fairy Queen, divide the rule of the land between them.

How Glooskap Made the Birds

Once upon a time, long before the white men came to Canada, there lived a wicked giant who caused great trouble and sorrow wherever he went. Men called him Wolf-Wind. Where he was born no man knows, but his home was in the Cave of the Winds, far in the north country in the Night-Night Land, and there men knew he was hiding on calm days when the sun was hot and the sea was still, and on quiet nights when not a leaf or a flower or a blade of grass was stirring. But whenever he appeared, the great trees cracked in fear and the little trees trembled and the flowers bent their heads close to the earth, trying to hide from his presence. Often he came upon them without warning and with little sign of his coming. And then the corn fell flat never to rise again, and tall trees crashed in the forest, and the flowers dropped dead because of their terror; and often the great waters grew white and moaned or screamed loudly or dashed themselves against the rocks trying to escape from

Wolf-Wind. And in the darkness of the night, when Wolf-Wind howled, there was great fear upon all the earth.

It happened once in those old times that Wolf-Wind was in a great rage, and he went forth to kill and devour all who dared to come in his path. It chanced in that time that many Indian families were living near the sea. The men and women were fishing far off the coast; they were catching fish to make food for the winter. They went very far away in small canoes, for the sea had long been still and they thought there was no danger. The little children were alone on shore. Suddenly, as the sun went down, without a sign of his coming, out of the north came Wolf-Wind in his great rage looking for prey and roaring loudly as he came. 'I am Wolf-Wind, the giant,' he howled. 'Cross not my path, for I will kill all the people I meet and eat them all up.' His anger only grew as he stalked along, and he splashed and tossed the waters aside in his fury as he came down upon the fishermen and fisherwomen far out to sea. The fishers had no time to get out of his reach or to paddle to the shore, so quick was Wolf-Wind's coming, and the giant caught them in his path and broke up their boats and killed them all. All night long he raged over the ocean looking for more fishers.

In the morning Wolf-Wind's anger was not yet spent. Far away in front of him he saw the little children of the fishers playing on the shore. He knew they were alone, for he had killed their fathers and mothers. He resolved to catch them and kill them too, and after them he went, still in a great rage. He went quickly towards the land, roaring as he went and dashing the waters against the

rocks in his madness. As he came near the beach he howled in his anger: 'I will catch you and kill you all and eat
you and bleach your bones upon the sand.' But the children heard him and they ran away as fast as they could,
and they hid in a cave among the great rocks and placed
a big stone at the mouth of the cave and Wolf-Wind
could not get in. He howled loudly at the door all day
and all night long, but the stone was strong and he could
not break it down. Then he went on his way still very
angry and still roaring, and he howled: 'I will come back
and catch you yet. You cannot escape from me.'

The children were very frightened, and they stayed
long in the cave after Wolf-Wind had gone, for far away
they could still hear him howling and crashing in the
forest. Then they came out. They knew that Wolf-Wind
had killed their fathers and mothers on the sea. They ran
away into the forest, for they thought that there they
would be safe. They went to the Willow-Willow Land
where they found a pleasant place with grass and flowers
and streams. And between them and the north country
where Wolf-Wind lived were many great trees with thick
leaves which they knew would protect them from the
giant.

But one day Wolf-Wind, true to his promise, came
again in a rage to find them. He came into the land killing all he met in his path. But he could not catch the
children, for the trees with their thick leaves kept him
away. They heard him howling in the forest far distant.
For many days in the late summer he tried to find them,
but their home was close to the trees, and the great
branches spread over them and the thick leaves saved
them, and only the sun from the south, coming from the

Summer-Flower country, could look in upon them. Try as he could with all his might, old Wolf-Wind could not harm them, although he knew that they were there; and they were always safe while they lived in the Willow-Willow Land.

Wolf-Wind was more angry than ever because of his failure, for he liked to feed on little children, and his rage knew no bounds. He swore that he would have vengeance on the trees. So he came back again and he brought with him to aid him another giant from the north country who had with him a strange and powerful charm, the Charm of the Frost. And the two giants tried to kill the trees that had saved the little children. But over many of the trees they had no power, for when they came, the trees only laughed and merely swayed and creaked and said: 'You cannot harm us; we are strong, for we came at first from the Night-Night Land in the far north country, and over us the Charm of the Frost has no power.' These were the Spruce and the Fir, the Hemlock and the Pine and the Cedar.

But on the other trees Wolf-Wind had vengeance as

he had vowed. One night, when the harvest moon was shining in the sky, he came without warning, and with the help of the giant bearing the Charm of the Frost he killed all the leaves that had kept him from the children and threw them to the ground. One after one the leaves came off from the Beech and the Birch, the Oak and the Maple, the Alder and the Willow. Some fell quickly, some fluttered slowly down, and some took a long time in dying. But at last the trees stood bare and cold against the sky and there was stillness and sadness in the forest. And Wolf-Wind laughed and played in silence through the leafless branches with the giant from Night-Night Land. And he said: 'Now I have overcome the leaves that kept me away, and now when I please I can kill the children.' But the children only moved closer to the strong and sturdy trees that had come at first from the far north country and over which the Charm of the Frost had no power, and Wolf-Wind could not reach them and they were still forever safe from the giants.

The children were very sad when they saw what Wolf-Wind had done to their friends and protectors, the trees. Summer had gone back to the Southland, following as she always did the Rainbow Road to her home in the Wilderness of Flowers. It was lonely now in the forest, and silent; there was not a whisper in the trees; there were no leaves, for it was autumn and Wolf-Wind had killed them all.

At last it came to that time of year when Glooskap, who ruled upon the earth and was very great in those days, gave his yearly gifts to little children. And he came into the land on a sled drawn by his faithful dogs to find out for himself what the children wished for. And the chil-

dren all came to him each asking for a boon. Now Glooskap had great power upon the earth in that old time. He
could always do what he willed. And the little children
whom Wolf-Wind had tried to harm in his rage came to
Glooskap, the Magic Master of gifts, and they were all
very sad because the leaves had gone.

'What do you wish?' said Glooskap.

'We wish nothing for ourselves,' said the children, 'but
we ask that the leaves that were killed by Wolf-Wind
because they saved us from his rage be brought back to
life and put back again in their old home in the trees.'

Glooskap was silent for a long time, and he sat and
thought as was his custom, and he smoked hard at his
mighty pipe, for he was a great smoker.

Now in that time there were no little forest birds upon
the earth, for Glooskap had not yet brought them into
being. There were only the birds that dwelt near the sea
and over whom Wolf-Wind had no power—Sea-gull and
Crane, Wild Duck and Loon, Kingfisher and Brant and
Curlew. These only laughed at the giant in his rage and
screamed in mockery as they flew from him and hid when
he came, among the shallows or the rocks or the thick
grass in the marshes. And there were also the sturdy birds
that dwelt with men and worked for them, giving them
eggs and food. These were Hen and Goose and Duck and
Wild Turkey. They gave men food, but they were not
fair to look upon; they waddled along and could not fly
well and they made no sweet music upon the earth, for
their song was a quack and a cackle.

Glooskap decided to bring other birds into the world
—not to give food but to bring happiness to the children
on the days when summer dwells in the land, with their

pretty feathers and their pleasant songs. So after he had smoked long in silence he hit upon a plan. And he said to the children asking for their yearly gifts: 'I cannot bring back to the trees the leaves that Wolf-Wind has killed and stripped off, for it is now too late. But I will take the fallen leaves and change them into little birds. And the birds shall never forget how they were born. When autumn comes they shall go with summer far away to the Summer-Flower Land, but in the springtime they shall always come back and they shall live as close as they can to the leaves from which they have sprung. And they shall nest, most of them, in the trees under the leaves, and even those that nest in the grass shall love the trees and linger in them. And they shall all be beautiful in colour like the leaves that gave them birth; and they shall have power to rest at times upon the air like a leaf fluttering; and the voice of the air and the laughing waters shall be in their throats and they shall sing sweet songs for little children. And I give the children charge over them to keep them from harm just as the leaves which gave them birth have saved the little children from the giants. And I will give the trees that Wolf-Wind has stripped, power to bring forth new leaves every spring-time so that when Summer comes back from the Wilder-ness of Flowers, the trees shall not be bare. And although Wolf-Wind may strip them off when the Giant of the Frost comes with him from the Night-Night Land, they shall always be replaced in the springtime. And I will take away much of Wolf-Wind's power so that he can no longer harm little children as wickedly as he has done before.'

Glooskap waved his magic wand as was his custom, and

at once great flocks of little birds sprang from the ground where the fallen leaves had lain. And they twittered and sang in a great chorus and flew back to the trees. They were of beautiful colours like the leaves that had given them birth. There were Robin Redbreasts and Thrushes all brown and red from the red and brown leaves of the Oak. And there were Finches and Hummingbirds all yellow and green and brown from the leaves of the Alder and the Willow, and they glowed like willows in the sunlight and fluttered like a leaf upon the air. There were Yellowbirds and Canadian Warblers from the golden Beech and Birch leaves. And there were Scarlet Tanagers and Orioles and Grosbeaks, all of changing colours—red and purple and brown—from the leaves of the Canadian Maple. And they all sang to the children and the children were all very happy again.

Then Glooskap sent the little birds all away to a warm country until the rule of the Giant of the Frost from the Night-Night Land was over, for it was winter in all the land and it was very cold. But in the springtime the little birds always come back from the Summer-Flower Land. And they build their nests among the trees as close as they can to their kindred, the leaves from which they came. And all day long they sing among the leaves for little children. At daybreak they wake the children with their choir of dawn, and at twilight they lisp and twitter to lull the children to sleep. And at night they hide among the leaves from Wolf-Wind and are very still with never a twitter or a song. For they do not forget that they are the children's gift from Glooskap and that they came from the leaves stripped from the trees by Wolf-Wind because the leaves saved the little children from the giant long ago.

The Fall of the Spider Man

In olden times the Spider Man lived in the sky-country.
He dwelt in a bright little house all by himself, where
he weaved webs and long flimsy ladders by which people
went back and forth from the sky to the earth. The Star-
people often went at night to earth where they roamed
about as fairies of light, doing good deeds for women and
little children, and they always went back and forth on
the ladder of the Spider Man. The Spider Man had to
work very hard, weaving his webs, and spinning the yarn
from which his ladders were made. One day when he had
a short breathing-time from his toil, he looked down at
the earth-country and there he saw many of the earth-
people playing at games, or taking sweet sap from the
maple trees, or gathering berries on the rolling hills; but
most of the men were lazily idling and doing nothing.
The women were all working, after the fashion of Indians
in those days; the men were working but little. And
Spider Man said to himself: 'I should like to go to the

earth-country where men idle their time away. I would marry four wives who would work for me while I would take life easy, for I need a rest.'

He was very tired of his work for he was kept at it day and night, always spinning and weaving his webs. But when he asked for a rest he was not allowed to stop; he was only kicked for his pains and called 'Sleepy-head', and 'Lazy-bones', and other harsh names, and told to work harder. Then he grew angry and he resolved to punish the Star-people because they kept him so hard at work. He thought that if he punished them and made himself a nuisance, they would be glad to be rid of him. So he hit upon a crafty plan. Each night when a Star-fairy was climbing back to the sky-country, just as he came near the top of the ladder, the Spider Man would cut the strands and the fairy would fall to earth with a great crash. Night after night he did this, and he chuckled to himself as he saw the sky-fairies sprawling through the air and kicking their heels while the earth-people looked up wonderingly at them and called them Shooting Stars. Many Star-people fell to earth in this way because of the Spider Man's tricks, and they could never get back to the sky-country because of their broken limbs or their disfigured faces, for in the sky-country the people all must have beautiful faces and forms. But Spider Man's tricks brought him no good; the people would not drive him away because they needed his webs and he was kept always at his tasks. At last he decided to run away of his own accord, and, one night when the Moon and the Stars had gone to work and the Sun was asleep, he said farewell to the sky-country and let himself down to earth by one of his own strands of yarn, spinning it as he dropped down.

In the earth-country he married four wives as he had planned, for he wanted them to work for him while he took his ease. He thought he had worked long enough. All went well for a time and the Spider Man was quite happy living his lazy and contented life. Not a strand did he spin nor a web did he weave. No men on earth were working—only the women toiled.

At last Glooskap, who ruled upon the earth in that time, became very angry because the men in these parts were so lazy, and he sent Famine into their country to punish them for their sins. Famine came very stealthily into the land and gathered up all the corn and carried it off; then he called to him all the animals and the birds and the fish of the sea and river, and he took them away with him. In all the land there was nothing left to eat. Only water remained. The people were very hungry and they lived on water for many days. Sometimes they drank the water cold, sometimes hot, sometimes luke-warm, but at best it was but poor fare. The Spider Man soon grew tired of this strange diet, for it did not satisfy his hunger to live always on water. It filled his belly and swelled him to a great size, but it brought him little nourishment or strength. So he said: 'There must be good food somewhere in the world. I will go in search of it.'

That night, when all the world was asleep, he took a large bag and crept softly away from his four wives and set out on his quest for food. He did not want anyone to know where he was going. For several days he travelled, living only on water; but he found no food, and the bag was still empty on his back. At last one day he saw birds in the trees and he knew that he was near the border of the Hunger-land.

That night in the forest, when he stopped at a stream to drink, he saw a tiny gleam of light far ahead of him through the trees. He hurried towards the light and soon he came upon a man with a great hump on his shoulders and scars on his face and a light hanging at his back with a shade on it which he could close and open at his will. The Spider Man said: 'I am looking for food; tell me where I can find it.' And the humped man with the light said: 'Do you want it for your people?' But the Spider Man said: 'No, I want it for myself.' Then the humped man laughed and said: 'You are near to the border of the Land of Plenty; follow me and I will give you food.' Then he flashed the light at his back, opening and closing the shade so that the light flickered, and he set off quickly through the trees.

The Spider Man followed the light flashing in the darkness, but he had to go so fast that he was almost out of breath when he reached the house where the humped man had stopped. But the humped man only laughed when he saw the Spider Man coming, puffing wearily along with his fat and swollen belly. He gave him a good fat meal and the Spider Man soon felt better after his long fast.

Then the humped man said: 'You are the Spider Man who once weaved webs in the sky. I, too, once dwelt in the star-country, and one dark night, as I was climbing back from the earth-country on your ladder, carrying my lamp on my back to light the way, when I was near the sky you cut the strands of the web and I fell to the earth with a great crash. That is why I have a great hump on my back and scars on my face, and because of this I have never been allowed to go back to the sky-country of the stars. I roam the earth at nights as a forest fairy just as I did in the olden days, for I have my former power still with me and I still carry my lamp at my back; it is the starlight from the sky-country. I shall never get back to the star-country while I have life. But some day when my work on earth is done I shall go back. But although you were cruel to me, I will give you food.'

The Spider Man remembered the nights he had cut the ladder strands, and he laughed to himself at the memory of the star-fairies falling to earth with a great crash. But the man with the light knew that now he had his chance to take vengeance on the Spider Man. The latter did not suspect evil. He was glad to get food at last.

Then the humped man said: 'I will give you four pots. You must not open them until you get home. They will then be filled with food, and thereafter always when you open them they will be packed with good food, and the food will never grow less.' The Spider Man put the four pots in his bag and, slinging it over his shoulder, he set out for his home, well pleased with his success. After he had gone away, the humped man used his power to make him hungry. Yet for several days he travelled without opening the pots, for, although he was almost starving, he wished to do as the humped man had told him.

At last he could wait no longer. He stopped near his home, took the pots out of the bag, and opened them. They were filled with good food as he had been promised. In one was a fine meat stew; in another were many cooked vegetables; in another was bread made from Indian corn; and in another was luscious ripe fruit. He ate until he was full. He covered the pots, put them back in the bag, and hid the bag among the trees. Then he went home.

He had meanwhile taken pity on his people and he decided to invite the Chief and all the tribe to a feast the next evening, for the pots would be full and the food would never decrease and there would be enough for all. He thought the people would regard him as a very wonderful man if he could supply them all with good food in their hunger.

When he reached his home his wives were very glad to see him back and they at once brought him water, the only food they had. But he laughed them to scorn and threw the water in their faces and said: 'Oh, foolish women! I do not want water; it is not food for a great man like me. I have had a good meal of meat stew and corn bread and cooked vegetables and luscious ripe fruit. I know where much food is to be found, but I alone know. I can find food when all others fail, for I am a great man. Go forth and invite the Chief and all the people to a feast which I shall provide for them tomorrow night—a feast for all the land, for my food never grows less.' They were all amazed when they heard his story, and the thought of his good meal greatly added to their hunger. But they went out and summoned all the tribe to a feast as he had told them.

The next night all the people gathered for the feast, for the news of it had spread through the land. They had taken no water that day, for they wished to eat well and they were very hungry—they were as hungry as wild beasts in search of food. The Spider Man was very glad because the people praised him, and he proudly brought in his bag of pots. The people all waited hungrily and eagerly. But when he uncovered the first pot there was no food there; he uncovered all the pots, but not a bit of food was in any of them. They were all empty, and in the bottom of each was a great gaping hole.

Now it had happened in this way. When the humped man, the Star-fairy, had given the pots to the Spider Man, he knew well that the Spider Man would disobey his orders and that he would open the pots before he reached his home. He chuckled to himself, for he knew that now he could take vengeance on the web-weaver who had injured him. So when the Spider Man had left the pots among the trees, the humped man used his magic power and made holes in the pots, and the charm of the food was broken and all the food disappeared. When the people saw the empty pots, they thought they had been purposely deceived. The remains of the food and the smell of stew and of fruit still clung to the pots. They thought the Spider Man had eaten all the food himself. So in their great hunger and their rage and their disappointment they fell upon him and beat him and bore him to the ground, while the humped man with the lamp at his back, hiding behind the trees, looked on and laughed in his glee.

Then the people split the Spider Man's arms to the shoulders, and his legs to the thighs, so that he had eight limbs instead of four. And the humped man—the Star-fairy named Firefly—came forth from behind the trees and, standing over the fallen Spider Man, he said: 'Henceforth, because of your cruelty to the star-people you will always crawl on eight legs, and you will have a fat round belly because of the water you have drunk; and sometimes you will live on top of the water. But you shall always eat only flies and insects. And you will always spin downwards but never upwards, and you will often try to get back to the star-country, but you shall always slip down again on the strand of yarn you have spun.' Then Firefly flashed his light and went quickly away, opening and closing the shade of his lamp as he flitted among the trees.

And to this day the Spider Man lives as the humped man of the lamp had spoken, because of the cruelty he practised on the Star-fairies in the olden days.

How Turtle Came

On the shores of a great water in Canada is a land where Indians once dwelt. In the days of French rule it was a garrisoned fort. The remains of the old moat and ramparts and stockade are still seen in the centre of what is now a large green meadow; but they are now overgrown with grass, and should you go there, on summer days you can see children playing upon them, picking wild flowers and making daisy chains, unmindful of the past fortunes of the spot on which they play. Behind you across the river which empties here is a city in modern dress. Before you is the sea with two little islands not far away resting in the summer haze upon its bosom. Moaning gas-buoys toss about in the gentle roll of the waters; by night red beacon lights lift their bright heads all about to light the sailor's road; summer cottages nestle on the beach before you; the hum of modern life is in your ears and the sight of it is in your eyes as you stand today upon the cliff.

But it was not always so. Long before the coming of the white race, before beacon lights and cities and summer cottages were known, this land was the home of Indians. Many of their descendants live there still, at peace with the white folk who took their lands and their forests. They are the remnants of Glooskap's people. It was here, on the beach in the little cove, that the Turtle was first created and where he first dwelt. Long ago, after the white men came, he fled from these waters; and although his descendants are still sometimes caught by fishermen off the coast, neither he nor his children nor any of his tribe ever went back to the place of his creation. But the place of his birth is still pointed out.

It was in Glooskap's time that the Turtle came into being. There dwelt in the land an old Indian, a lazy, poor, and by no means beautiful man. As a hunter he had been of no value; he lived alone; and now he had come to the end of his life with little of the world's goods to his credit. But although he was poor, he was of a merry heart and a good nature, and he was well liked by all. Now the Chief of the tribe had three beautiful daughters who were much sought for by the young men of the village, all of whom wished to win their love. The eldest was the loveliest in the land; her name was Flower of the Corn. The old Indian would gladly have made one of these girls his wife, for he was tired of living alone, but she on her part thought him worthless, and he on his part feared that if he wooed her, her many other suitors would be jealous and would perhaps take his life. So the old man kept his secret to himself and continued his sad existence.

It happened that one day Glooskap came into the land

to see his people. Of all the tents in the village he chose that of the old man as his resting place, for he had known him a long time and liked him because of his good nature and his merry heart. He was not with him long before he knew his secret, that he loved Flower of the Corn; and he also learned of his fear to woo her. Glooskap encouraged him and urged him to make his wishes known to the Chief. But the old Indian said: 'I am old and poor and I have no good clothes to wear, and I know that I should meet only with scorn.' But Glooskap placed upon him his magic belt, and at once the old man became young and handsome; he also gave him fine clothes. Then he sent him to the Chief's home. And the old man said, after the fashion of Indians when they wish to marry: 'I am tired living alone. I have come for your eldest daughter.' And the old Chief, when he saw him so beautiful because of Glooskap's magic power, could not refuse his request, and Flower of the Corn became his bride.

As the old man had feared, the young men of the village were very angry because he had won so beautiful a wife, and they resolved to do him harm. At first they tried to take vengeance on Glooskap, for as they had seen little of him, they did not know of his great power. A great wedding feast was held for the old man and his bride, to which all the young men were invited. Two of the most jealous sat next to Glooskap, one on each side, and during the feast they plotted to kill him. But Glooskap heard them plotting against his life and he knew that the time had come to show his strength. So at the end of the wedding feast, as they arose from the table, he turned to each one and tapped him gently on the nose. When each rubbed the spot that Glooskap had touched, he found that his nose had disappeared. In great shame and anger they fled from the feast and never afterwards dwelt among men. One of these was Toad; the other was Porcupine. And since that time neither Toad nor Porcupine has ever had a nose, and their faces have always been flat because of Glooskap's touch at the banquet long ago.

Some days after the wedding feast, a great festival was held in the village. Glooskap knew that here again an attempt would be made upon the old Indian's life by his jealous enemies. He feared too that after he had gone from the village his old friend would surely be treacherously killed, and, as the time of his going away was at hand, he resolved upon a plan to save him from danger. He told the old man that at the festival his enemies would try to trample him under their feet during a game of ball. And he gave him a magic root which, if he ate it before the game, would give him power to jump high when they crowded in upon him. Sure enough, in the game of ball the young men surrounded the old man and watched for a chance to crush him. Twice he jumped high over their heads and escaped unhurt. But the third time, when he jumped, he stuck upon the top of a tent and could not get down.

Inside the tent sat Glooskap quietly smoking his pipe and waiting for this very thing to happen. He made a smouldering fire from which the smoke rose in great clouds and passed out at the top of the tent around the old man, and he smoked and smoked great pipefuls of tobacco until far into the night. And the old man hung to the tent poles, dangling in the smoke until midnight. He hung there so long that from the smoke of the smouldering fire and that of Glooskap's pipe, his old skin became as hard as a shell. And Glooskap said to him: 'I have done this thing for your own good. I fear that if I leave you here, after I have gone your enemies will kill you. I make you now chief of the Tortoise race and your name shall be called Turtle; hereafter you may roll through a flame of fire and you will not be burned nor will you feel pain, and you may live in water or on land as you prefer. And you shall have a very long life; and although your head be cut off you shall live nine days afterwards. And when your enemies throw you into the fire or into the water, you need have no fear.' Then he took him down from the tent pole.

The next day the old Indian's enemies, angry because he had escaped at the festival, built a great fire in the forest and, seizing him as he walked alone in the woods, they threw him upon it. But he went to sleep in the flame, and when he awoke he called for more wood, telling them that he was very cold. They wondered greatly, and after plotting together they resolved to throw him into the sea. They carried him far out in a canoe and dropped him overboard, and went ashore well pleased with their work, for they believed that at last they had taken vengeance. The next day was a day of great heat. At low tide, when some of his enemies looked out to sea, they saw basking in the sun on a sand-bar far away a strange figure. They were curious, and they rowed out to see what it was that shone so brightly in the sun. When they reached the sand-bar after paddling a long time they saw that it was the old Indian. There he was, sunning himself on the sand-bar, his hard smoked back shining in the bright light. As they came near, he said, 'Good day', and, grinning at them mischievously, he rolled lazily off the sand-bar and disappeared in the water.

Glooskap, before he left the island, used his magic power to change Flower of the Corn in the same way, and he sent her into the sea to live with her husband. And he gave her power to lay eggs in the sand. And the two lived happily for many long years and raised up a mighty race. But still the Turtle rolls sideways into the sea like his old ancestor if men come near him as he suns himself on the sand. And you can still see on his back the marks of Glooskap's smoke. When the white men came, he left the land of his creation, but his descendants to this day live to a great age and grow to a great size along the Atlantic coast.

The Partridge and His Drum

In far-back times when only Indians dwelt in Canada, Glooskap, who was Lord and Master of the tribes, chose Partridge from among all his creatures to be the boat-builder for the birds of the sea. Partridge was then a very wonderful bird, very different from what he is today. He dwelt always along the ocean shore, on the banks of great rivers, and he could swim like a duck or a gull. He could change his shape to that of a man. He knew all the country well, and often he wandered far through the woods looking for good trees from which to build his boats. Among all the people he was held in high regard because of his skill. He was always industrious and always busy, and at all hours of the day and late into the night he could be heard hammering at his canoes, making a sound like a man tapping quickly on a drum. But he lost his reputation through no fault of his own. He no longer builds boats; the power to make the strange sound of his hammering is all that remains with him of his former greatness.

It happened that one very cold day Partridge walked alone over the snow in the deep forest near the shore of a great lake, looking for lumber for his boats. On the bank of a stream he saw four beautiful maidens sitting on the ice braiding their long hair. He knew that they were nymphs or fairies of the stream, and he watched them from behind a tree. He had long desired to win a stream fairy for his bride, but up to that time he had found it an impossible task, for the fairies were very timid. As he watched them now, he thought to himself: 'Perhaps I can catch one of them and carry her off.' So he stealthily slipped from behind the tree and crept along towards the bank. But the water-nymphs, who could hear the smallest sound, heard his footsteps and, looking around, they spied him among the trees. 'Oh, oh!' they all cried, and at once they all dropped into the icy water and disappeared.

Now Partridge, being then a river-dweller and of very great strength, was a good fisherman. Many a time he had caught the slippery harbour seals and often he had dined plentifully on their meat. He hit upon a crafty trick by which to seize a nymph. He cut a number of branches from a spruce tree and, sticking them upright in the snow on the shore, he hid behind them and waited for the nymphs to appear again. Sure enough they soon came back and sat again upon the ice, braiding their long hair. Partridge put his head over the boughs to take a peep at them so that he might pick out the most beautiful, but again they saw him, and with the same frightened cry, 'Oh, oh!' they dropped quickly into the sea. After them went Partridge, although he knew that the water was very cold. He caught one, but she slipped from his

arms, and when he came to the surface he had only her hair-ribbon in his hand.

Now in those old days water-nymphs in this part of the sea could not live long without their hair-ribbons, for the ribbons contained always much of their magic power. Partridge knew this, and he knew too that sooner or later the nymph would wander about on land looking for her lost charm. So he put the ribbon in his pocket and with a light heart he went about his business of seeking wood for his boats. That night when he went back to his tent he hid the ribbon not far from his hand in hope of the fairy's visit; then, pretending to sleep, he closed his eyes and waited. He had not been there long when there came in very softly the beautiful water-nymph in search of her lost ribbon. Now when a water-nymph sets foot in the dwelling of man or animal without her hair-ribbon, she is always powerless. This Partridge knew well. He sprang quickly from his couch, caught her with little trouble, and easily persuaded her to remain with him as his wife. This was against Glooskap's orders, for Glooskap knew that if one of his people married a water-nymph, no good could come of it. But Glooskap said nothing.

Partridge and his nymph-wife lived happily enough for a time. But he always feared for her safety when he went far away looking for lumber for his boats, for many evil creatures were always about in the forest. And he always said to her before he went away: 'Keep the doors tightly barred while I am gone, for many wicked people and robbers prowl through the woods, and they will try to enter the tent—perhaps to kill you.' And she always promised to be on her guard.

One day Partridge went far away in search of lumber

for a new fleet of boats he was then building. In the afternoon he came to a grove of wonderful cedar trees. He wished to examine it carefully, and as night was coming on—for winter nights come early in the Canadian woods —he decided to stay there until the next day. So as the day went down, he made a bed of boughs and went to sleep. He had no fear for his wife's safety, for she had promised to keep the doors barred.

Meanwhile his wife waited at home for his coming. When the stars came out she knew that he would not come home that night, and, being sleepy, she went to bed, first seeing that the doors were securely fastened. She felt very lonely all by herself in the big tent, for Partridge, because of the troublesome noise of his boat-building, dwelt a good distance away from his neighbours. At midnight she was awakened by a loud knocking at the door. 'Open the door,' said a voice outside, 'I am cold and hungry and I have come far.' But mindful of the warning of Partridge, the nymph-wife paid no heed to the call. Now the voice was that of a wicked sorcerer who always prowled through the forest and who knew that Partridge was away. He wished to kill and eat the nymph. He was a very clever and sly fellow, and he could imitate the voices of all men and animals to lure people to their death. For a long time after his first call he was silent. Then he knocked again and imitated the voice of the nymph's brothers and sisters and said: 'Oh, sister, we have followed you for a long time until at last we have found you. Open the door to us.' But still the nymph was suspicious and refused to unbar the door. Then the sorcerer imitated her father's voice and called her 'daughter'. But still she would not let him in. At last he talked like her mother and said: 'Oh, daughter, open the door. I have come far in search of you, and I am very cold and hungry and tired.' The nymph-wife was deceived at last, for she thought the voice was that of her old mother from the stream. Hastily she opened the door. At once the wicked sorcerer—the evil spirit of the woods—pounced upon her and, killing her at a blow, he greedily devoured her like a wolf, until not a bone was left.

The next morning Partridge came home. He found the door of his house open and his wife absent. He wondered greatly, for he remembered her promise and he could not believe that she had been killed. So he resolved to use his magic power to learn where she had gone. He took his magic wooden plate and filled it with water and placed it in a corner of the tent while he slept. When he awoke, the dish was full, not of water but of blood, and he knew from this sign that his wife had been killed by the sorcerer. He determined to punish her slayer and, taking his axe and his bow and arrows and his magic charm, he left his work and set out in pursuit of the sorcerer. He knew that the sorcerers travelled in pairs; he knew too that they had many tricks by which to escape punishment and that they could take on various shapes. So he went along cautiously.

By evening he reached a great lone land in the far north where he thought he found traces of two of the evil ones. He came to a large cave which he entered, intending to pass the night there. From a huge rock at the side of the cave a man's foot was sticking. He knew that here was one of the sorcerers (who had gone into the rock to sleep as was their custom), leaving his foot sticking out so that his comrade could pull him out when he had slept long enough. Partridge quickly cut off the foot close to the rock, and there the sorcerer was left closed up forever in the stone. There the rock remains to this day.

Just as Partridge had finished the cutting, the sorcerer's companion came in, and Partridge knew—for he had seen him often about his tent—that here at last was the murderer of his wife. When the sorcerer saw no foot sticking from the rock, he knew at once that his brother was forever locked up in the stone, and he became very angry. Then he saw Partridge, whom he knew to be his brother's slayer, but giving no sign of his knowledge, he received him kindly. He bolted the door of the cave and then made a great fire thinking to roast Partridge alive and thereby have a good meal. But Partridge used his magic charm against heat and helped the sorcerer to pile more wood on the fire, saying that he was very cold. Soon the cave grew hotter and hotter until at last its sides became red and the flames shot high to the roof, and even before he knew it the sorcerer was overcome by the great heat. Partridge threw him upon the fire, where he was quickly burned to cinders. Then, well pleased with his vengeance, he returned quickly to his home.

But from that day poor Partridge was never himself again. He sorrowed greatly for his dead nymph-wife until he became stupid and could not do his work well, but he went faithfully about his duties, finishing the great fleet of boats for the birds and animals. Finally came the day when all were to be launched, and Glooskap and all his people gathered to see the fleet go by. It was a very wonderful sight on a great inland sea. The eagle had a large canoe which he paddled with the ends of his wings; all the birds of the sea and the river had very wonderful boats—the crane and the duck, the snipe and the curlew, the plover and the gull, the wild goose and the loon and the kingfisher. And the boats were all of different colours, each colour the same as that of the bird for whom the boat was made. All the birds were supplied with boats. Even the humming-bird had a tiny canoe of many wonderful colours, and he had a little paddle not larger than a small pin.

Partridge's own canoe was the last to be launched. The people all watched for it in patience and eagerness, for they thought that because he had built such wonderful

boats for other birds, he would have a particularly good one for himself.

Now Partridge had built his own canoe last while he sorrowed for his dead wife. His brain had been muddled by his great grief. He reasoned foolishly that since a boat with two ends could be rowed in two directions, a boat with no ends at all could be rowed in all directions. So he made his own boat round like a saucer. But when it was launched and he tried to paddle it, he made no headway, for it turned round and round but always stayed in one place. All the people and the birds when they saw it laughed heartily at him and called him 'Fool'.

Then poor Partridge's grief was increased. He knew that he had forever lost his reputation as a boat-builder among the birds of the sea. He had no wish to dwell longer among them, and he decided to leave them forever. So he flew far away into the forest, and since that time he has never been seen upon the shore of the sea, nor near a river or lake. He stays on land, far in the deep woods, and he has forgotten even how to fish and how to swim. But he still keeps one remnant of his old life. He still makes a drumming noise as if he is hammering a canoe, and deep in the forest you can still hear his strange sound. You know then that he is mindful of old times when he built boats upon the shore, and all day long and far into the night tapped lightly with his hammer.

The First Mosquito

When Glooskap lived with his people it happened once
that the tribes grew jealous of his power. This jealousy
was not because of any evil in themselves; it was prompted
by a wicked sorceress who, during the absence of Glooskap, prevailed upon the people to do him harm. Some
said that the sorceress was angry because she had once
loved Glooskap and he had refused to return her love;
others said that she was much older than Glooskap, that
before his birth she had herself ruled the earth for a long
time, and that when Glooskap came he had put an end
to her reign. The truth of the matter no man knows, but
it is certain that she was very powerful and that she
always watched for a chance to harm Glooskap.

Her chance came when Glooskap went for six weeks
on a hunting trip far into the forest. She then told the
people that he was neglecting them, and she soon persuaded them to pack up and leave him, for she believed
that he would perish if he were left alone. When the

people went away, they took with them Dame Bear,
Glooskap's old grandmother, and his little brother, whom
Glooskap had left behind. The band journeyed hastily
across the land to the sea; then they sailed in their canoes
to a great island, where they stopped and set up their
tents. And the sorceress left the road they travelled well
guarded by evil beasts and dragons who, she hoped,
would kill Glooskap if he tried to follow them. She made
Dame Bear and the little boy her slaves, and compelled
them to do much hard work. She gave them but little
food and but scanty clothing, so that they were soon very
miserable.

When Glooskap came back to his home at the end of
six weeks, he found that his people had disappeared. His
friend Fox, who had watched slyly the people's departure
and the wicked woman's tricks, told him all that had
happened. Glooskap did not blame his people, for he
knew that their going away had been brought about by
his old enemy. But that he might teach his people the
folly of their act—for he knew that they would now be
very hungry and poor—he tarried alone in his homeland
for many years before he set out to find them and to take
vengeance on their wicked leader. Then, taking his magic
belt and his two dogs, he set out upon his long journey.
He went across the sea to another land, and then he travelled eastward, his dogs following close behind him. Here
he was far from the road that his people had travelled
and there were no dragons to bar his progress.

Soon he came to a village where the people were
friendly. He heard from an old man and woman about
the road along which the sorceress and his own people
had passed. The old man told him of the dragons ahead

of him and of the evil, hideous creatures that had been left to guard the way. But Glooskap, unafraid, and trusting in his dogs and his magic belt, set out along the enchanted road. At last he came to a narrow pass in the hills watched over by two terrible dogs. He put his magic belt around the necks of his own dogs for a moment and at once they grew to an immense size; and they easily killed the beasts of his enemy and he passed on unharmed.

After some hours he came to a high hill. At the bottom was a large tent in which he knew, from the tale of the old man of the friendly village, that a wicked man lived with his two beautiful daughters. He knew too that they waited his coming, for, prompted by the sorceress, they wished to kill him. As he looked down from the top of the hill, he saw the two daughters approaching afar off. They were very beautiful and fair; but Glooskap remembered the old man's warning and he resolved to be on his guard. One of them carried in her hands a string of costly beads. They met him with pleasant smiles and invited him to the tent below the hill; and they tried to place the beads about his neck to show him their great love. But Glooskap knew that the beads were enchanted, and that if he placed them around his neck he should lose his strength and power. So he set his dogs upon the girls, and the dogs were so terrible because of his magic belt that the girls ran away in great fear; as they ran, they dropped the string of beads, without which they had no power. Glooskap picked up the beads and then cautiously entered the tent of his enemies. On a couch of skins near the door the old man was dozing, and before he could rise, Glooskap placed the beads about his neck and killed him with a blow. Then he went on his way. He met with many enemies on this evil road, but by the aid of his dogs and his magic belt and the enchanted beads he overcame them all and was unharmed.

At last he reached the sea, and he looked over the dark water to another land and wondered how to get across. Finally he sang the magic song that the whales always obeyed. Old Blob the Whale came quickly to his call, and getting on her back he sailed away to the eastward. His two dogs swam close behind Old Blob. The whale soon brought him to the land where he knew that his people dwelt. He sprang ashore, his dogs following him, and set out with long rapid strides in search of his enemies. At the end of a few hours' journey he found traces of old camp-fires, and he knew that his people were not far away. At last he reached the place where they were living. In the distance he saw a camp which, because of his magic power, he knew to be that of the sorceress. Near by was his little brother, whom the wicked sorceress had made her slave. He was pale and much worn, and he was clad only in rags; he was seeking wood for a fire, and as he gathered up the dry sticks he cried and sang a song of lament: 'Where is Glooskap, my big brother? Alas, he is far away, and I shall never see him again!' Then Glooskap took pity on his little brother and gave a signal that the little boy knew well. And his brother, turning around, spied Glooskap behind the trees afar off, and running to him cried out with joy, for he knew that help had at last come.

But Glooskap knew that to overcome his great enemy and to free his people he must be very careful and use his craftiest tricks. He told his little brother to be silent, and to tell no one but Old Dame Bear, the grandmother, that he had come. He sent him back to his hard work in the

camp and promised that when the twilight came he should be freed. And he said: 'Do what you can to make the wicked woman angry, for when anger comes to her, her power leaves her; when you are sent to rock her baby to sleep at twilight, snatch it from its cradle and throw it into the camp-fire. Then run to me where I hide here among the trees. Take Dame Bear with you and all will be well.'

His little brother then went back to his hard work in the woman's tent and told Dame Bear what he had seen and heard. And the two waited patiently for the twilight. At the sunset hour the little boy, still supperless, was sent by the sorceress to rock her baby to sleep. For the first time in his long separation from his big brother he worked with joy and without hunger, for he knew that he would soon be free. Suddenly he snatched from the cradle-hammock the woman's baby—a wicked child like her mother—and hurled her into the camp-fire. Then, taking Dame Bear by the arm, he ran towards Glooskap's hiding-place. The baby howled with pain and cursed loudly as she heard her mother do, and rolled herself out of the fire. And the sorceress was very angry, and muttering dire threats she ran after the boy and Dame Bear. They soon reached Glooskap, who sprang from his hiding-place, his magic belt around him. When the sorceress saw Glooskap, she was more angry than before, so that her strength left her and she was powerless. Yet she gave battle.

Glooskap tore up a huge pine tree from its roots and hurled it at his enemy. It entered her side and stuck there, and although she tried with all her might she could not draw it out. Glooskap could now have killed her with a blow, but he did not wish to do that. He wanted to let her live in misery, and to give her a greater punishment than death. And so, yelling with pain and shame, the sorceress ran back to her tent, while Glooskap took Dame Bear and his little brother to his own camp among the trees and gave them food. He knew now that the battle was over, for it had long been known that if the wicked woman's side was once pierced, her power would never return.

When Glooskap's people heard that he had come, they rejoiced greatly, for they were hungry and cold. The sorceress had failed to provide food for them, and they were tired of her wicked and cruel rule which was very unlike that of Glooskap. But Glooskap tarried before making friends again with them, and remained for many days in his own camp in the trees watching them from afar. His dogs guarded his grove and kept all away, except Dame Bear and his little brother. Meanwhile the wicked sorceress, in pain with the pine tree in her side, moved about in great anger, but as her power was now gone, the people refused longer to obey her. And they all laughed at her because of the pine tree sticking in her side. At last, being very angry, she said: 'I do not wish to live like this when my power is gone. All the people laugh at me because of the pine tree sticking in my side. I wish that I might change to something that would always be a plague and a torment to man, for I hate mankind.' Glooskap heard her wish, although he was afar off, and with his magic power he changed her at once to a mosquito. Then he forgave his people, and as they were hungry he gave them much food and drink, for he had killed many moose in the land. And the people all rejoiced and promised never again to forsake him or to be jealous of his power.

Then Glooskap gathered his people on the shore of the great ocean and, calling the whales, his sea-carriers, he bade them carry him and his people from this land back to their old home. There they settled down again in peace. But to this day the wicked sorceress roams over the earth as a mosquito; and the pine tree in her side is a sharp sting. She is never at rest, but she shall always remain as she wished, a torment to mankind. The only thing on earth she dreads is fire and smoke, for she still remembers that the throwing of her baby into the fire long ago caused the outburst of anger that in the end deprived her of her strength. And by fire and smoke in the summer twilight, men still drive her and her descendants from their dwellings.

How Rabbit Lost His Tail

When Glooskap first created the animals in Canada, he took good care that they should all be friendly to himself and to his people. They could all talk like men, and like them they had one common speech. Each had a special duty to do for Glooskap, and each did his best to help him in his work. Of all the animals, the gentlest and most faithful was Bunny the Rabbit. Now in those first days of his life, Rabbit was a very beautiful animal, more beautiful than he is today. He had a very long bushy tail like a fox; he always wore a thick brown coat; his body was large and round and sleek; his legs were straight and strong; he walked and ran like other animals and did not hop and jump about as he does now. He was always very polite and kind of heart. Because of his beauty and his good qualities, Glooskap chose him as his forest guide, his Scout of the Woods. He gave him power that enabled him to know well all the land so that he could lead people and all the other animals wherever they wished to go without losing their way.

One day in the springtime it chanced that Rabbit sat alone on a log in the forest, his long bushy tail trailing far behind him. He had just come back from a long scouting tour and he was very tired. As he sat resting in the sun, an Indian came along. The Indian was weary and stained with much travel, and he looked like a wayfarer who had come far. He threw himself on the ground close to the log on which Rabbit sat and began to weep bitterly. Rabbit, with his usual kindness, asked: 'Why do you weep?' And the man answered: 'I have lost my way in the forest. I am on my way to marry this afternoon a beautiful girl whom her father pledged to me long ago. She is loved by a wicked forest Fairy and I have heard that perhaps she loves him. And I know that if I am late she will refuse to wait for me and that she will marry him instead.' But Rabbit said: 'Have no fear. I am Rabbit, Glooskap's forest guide. I will show you the way and bring you to the wedding in good time.' The man was comforted and his spirits rose, and they talked some time together and became good friends.

When the man had somewhat got back his strength, they began their journey to the wedding. But Rabbit, being nimble-footed, ran fast and was soon so far in advance of his companion that he was lost to view. The man followed slowly, catching here and there through the green trees a glimpse of his guide's brown coat. As he stumbled along, thinking of his troubles, he fell into a deep pit that lay close to the forest path. He was too weak to climb out, and he called loudly for help. Rabbit soon missed his follower, but he heard the man's yells and, turning about, he ran back to the pit. 'Have no fear,' said Rabbit as he looked over the edge. 'I will get you out without mishap.' Then, turning his back to the pit, he let his long bushy tail hang to the bottom. 'Catch hold of my tail,' he ordered. 'Hold on tight and I will pull you out.' The man did as he was told. Rabbit sprang forward, but as he jumped, the weight of the man, who was very heavy, was more than he could bear, and poor Rabbit's tail broke off within an inch of the root. The man fell back into the pit with a thud, holding in his hand poor Rabbit's tail.

But Rabbit, in all his work as a guide, had never known defeat, and he determined not to know it now. Holding to a strong tree with his front feet, he put his hind legs into the pit and said to the man: 'Take hold of my legs and hang on tight.' The man did as he was told. Then Rabbit pulled and pulled until his hind legs stretched and he feared that they too would break off; but although the weight on them was great, he finally pulled the man out after great difficulty. He found to his dismay that his hind legs had lengthened greatly because of their heavy load. He was no longer able to walk straight, but he now had to hop along with a strange jumping gait. Even his body was much stretched, and his waist had become very slender because of his long heavy pull. The two travellers then went on their way, Rabbit hopping along, and the man moving more cautiously.

Finally they reached the end of their journey. The people were all gathered for the wedding and eagerly awaiting the coming of the bridegroom. Sure enough, the forest Fairy was there trying by his tricks to win the girl for himself. But the man was in good time, and he married the maiden as he had hoped. As he was very thankful to Rabbit, he asked him to the marriage dance and told him he might dance with the bride. So Rabbit put rings on his heels and a bangle around his neck, after his usual custom at weddings, and joined the merry-makers.

Through the forest green where they danced, many tiny streams were flowing, and to the soft music of these the dance went on. As the bride jumped across one of these streams during her dance with Rabbit, she accidentally let the end of her dress drop into the water so that it got very wet. When she moved again into the sun, her dress, because of its wetting, shrank and shrank until it reached her knees and made her much ashamed. But Rabbit's heart was touched as usual by her plight; he ran quickly and got a deer skin that he knew to be hidden in the trees not far away, and he wrapped the pretty skin around the bride. Then he twisted a cord with which to tie it on. He held one end of the cord in his teeth and twisted the other end with his front paws. But in his haste, he held it so tight and twisted it so hard that when a couple waltzing past carelessly bumped into him, the cord split his upper lip right up to the nose. But Rabbit was not dismayed by his split lip. He fastened on the bride's new deer-skin gown, and then he danced all the evening until the moon was far up in the sky. Before he went away, the man and his bride wanted to pay him for his work, but he would not take payment. Then the bride gave him a new white fur coat and said: 'In winter wear this white coat. It is the colour of snow; your enemies cannot then see you so plainly against the white ground, and they cannot so easily do you harm; but in summer wear your old brown coat, the colour of the leaves and grass.' And Rabbit gratefully took the coat and went his way.

He lingered many days in the new country, for he was ashamed to go back to his own people with his changed appearance. His lip was split, his tail was gone, and his hind legs were stretched and crooked. Finally he mustered up his courage and returned home. His old friends wondered much at his changed looks, and some of them were cruel enough to laugh at him. But Rabbit deceived them all. When they asked him where he had been so long, he answered: 'I guided a man to a far-off land which you have never seen and of which you have never heard.' Then he told them many strange tales of its beauty and its good people.

'How did you lose your fine tail?' they asked. And he answered: 'In the land to which I have been, the animals wear no tails. It is an aristocratic country, and wishing to be in the fashion, I cut mine off.'

'And why is your waist so slender?' they asked. 'Oh,' replied Rabbit, 'in that country it is not the fashion to be fat, and I took great trouble to make my waist slight and willowy.'

'Why do you hop about,' they asked, 'when you once walked so straight?' 'In that land,' answered Rabbit, 'it is not genteel to walk straight; only the vulgar and untrained do that. The best people have a walk of their own, and it took me many days under a good walking teacher to learn it.'

'But how did you split your upper lip?' they asked finally. 'In the land to which I have been,' said Rabbit, 'the people do not eat as we do. There they eat with knives and forks and not with their paws. I found it hard to get used to their new ways. One day I put food into my mouth with my knife—a very vulgar act in that land —and my knife slipped and cut my lip, and the wound has never healed.'

And being deceived, and envying Rabbit because of the wonders he had seen, they asked him no more questions. But the descendants of Rabbit to this day wear a white coat in winter and a brown one in summer. They have also a split upper lip; their waist is still very slender; they have no tail; their hind legs are longer than their front ones; they hop and jump nimbly about, but they are unable to walk straight. And all these strange things are a result of old Rabbit's accident at the man's wedding long ago.

How Rabbit Deceived Fox

Long ago in Indian days in Canada, when Rabbit worked for Glooskap as his forest guide, he was a great thief. He liked most of all to steal by moonlight, and he crept quietly into gardens and fields where Indian vegetables were growing, for he was very fond of cabbage and lettuce and beans. Not far from his home there lived alone an old widow woman who had no children. She could not hunt game because she was a woman, and she had never been trained to the chase, so she kept a little garden from which she made a good living. All day long from dawn until sunset she toiled hard, tilling her little garden, watering her vegetables, and keeping them free from weeds. And she grew green cabbages and red carrots and yellow beans and big fat pumpkins and Indian corn, which she traded with Indian hunters in return for fish and meat. In this way she always had plenty of food, and she lived very well on good fare. But Rabbit, going his rounds one day, discovered her garden, although it was

deep in the forest, and every night by moonlight or starlight he robbed it and grew sleek and fat from the results
of his thefts. And morning after morning the old widow
woman found that many cabbages and carrots were miss-
ing and that much harm had been done to her plants.
She had an idea that Rabbit was the pilferer, for she had
heard that he was a great thief, but she was not very sure.

She watched many nights, but she was never able to
catch the robber, so stealthily did he come, and it was
not easy to see him in the shadows. So she said to herself:
'I will set up a scarecrow, a figure in the shape of a little
man, and I will place it at my garden gate and it will
frighten away the robber, whoever he may be, for I must
save my vegetables or I shall starve when the cold winter
comes.'

She picked from the spruce and the fir trees close by
a great store of gum and balsam. This she formed into a
figure in the shape of a little man. She made two eyes
from glass beads that would shine like fire in the starlight, and a nose from a pine cone, and hair from the corn
tassels and yellow moss. Then she placed the figure at the
entrance to the garden where she knew the robber would
come. 'Now,' she thought, 'I will scare away the thief.'

When night fell and the moon rose above the trees,
Rabbit came along, as was his custom, to steal his nightly
meal. As he came near the garden very softly, he saw in
the moonlight what he thought was a man standing in
the path by the garden gate. The moon hung low over
the forest, and there was a thin grey mist on the earth,
for it was near to autumn and the nights were already
cool; and the figure of the little man looked larger than
human in the misty light, and it cast a long black shadow

like that of a giant on the grass. Rabbit was much afraid and he trembled like an aspen leaf, but he stood quiet behind a tree and watched the strange figure.

For a long time he stood still and watched and listened. But the strange figure did not move, and not a sound did Rabbit hear but the chirp of a cricket. Then with great caution he came closer. But still the figure did not move. Then his fear left him and he grew bolder, for he was very hungry and he could smell the vegetables and the wild honeysuckle in the still night air. So he walked bravely up to the little dummy man and said: 'Get out of my way and let me pass.' But the man did not move. Then Rabbit struck the man a sharp blow with his fist. But still the figure did not move. Rabbit's fist stuck fast in the gum and he could not pull it away. Then he struck out with his other fist, and it too, like the other, was held firm. 'I shall kick you,' said Rabbit in a rage. 'Take that,' and he struck out wildly with his foot. But his foot, like his fist, stuck fast. Then he kicked with the other foot, but that too was held in the gum. Rabbit was now very cross and in his anger he said: 'Now I shall bite you,' but when he bit the little man, his teeth, like his feet and hands, stuck fast. Then he pushed with his body with all his might, hoping to knock the little man down, but his whole body stuck to the dummy figure.

He cried out loudly, for he was now beside himself with fear, and the old woman, when she heard his yells, came running out of her house. 'Aha!' she said. 'So you are the robber who has been stealing from my garden. I will rid the world of a pilfering pest, for I will kill you this very night.' Then she pulled him away from the gum figure and put him in a strong bag and tied the mouth of the bag with a stout string. She left the bag on the path by the garden gate and went to look for her axe to kill Rabbit.

While Rabbit lay there wondering how he was going to escape, Fox came prowling along. He stumbled over the bag, for he did not see it in the shadows, and he plunged forward headlong to the ground with a great thud. He got up and rained kicks upon the bag. He was mad because he had been tripped. He kicked poor Rabbit's back until Rabbit cried in pain. 'Who are you in the bag?' asked Fox when he heard the cries. 'I am your friend Rabbit,' was the answer. 'What are you doing, hiding in the bag?' asked Fox. Then Rabbit suddenly thought of a way of escape. He knew that Fox had long been looking for a wife, but that no one would have him as no one trusted him because his fame for treachery and slyness was so great. 'I am not hiding,' he said. 'The old woman who owns this garden wants me to marry her grand-daughter, and when I refused to do it she caught me and shut me up in this bag; she has just gone to bring the girl from her house, for she is determined to make me marry her here in the moonlight this very night. I don't want to marry her, for she is very big and fat, and I am very small and lean.' Then he cried 'Boo-hoo-hoo' again, and Fox said: 'I have been looking for a wife for a long time, and I like fat people. Let me get into the bag in your place and I will marry the grand-daughter instead, for the old woman will not know me in the shadows.' And Rabbit gladly agreed. Then Fox untied the bag and let Rabbit out and got into the bag himself, and Rabbit tied up the mouth of the bag and hurried away as quickly as he could.

Soon the old woman came back, carrying her axe. She sharpened it on a stone and said: 'Now I will kill you, and you will thieve no more in my garden. A poor woman must live untroubled by such pilfering rogues.'

When Fox heard these words and the sound of the stone upon the axe, he knew that he had been deceived by Rabbit, and when the old woman opened the bag he sprang nimbly out with a sudden bound and was away before she could catch him. He swore by the starlight that he would have vengeance on Rabbit.

All night long he searched for him and all the next

day, but he could not find him. At last, in the gathering
twilight, he came upon him in an open space in the
forest on the other side of a stream, eating his fill of wild
vegetables. Fox tried to coax him across the stream to his
side, for he himself was afraid of the water, but Rabbit
would not go. 'Why don't you eat some cheese?' said
Rabbit. 'There is a big round cheese in the stream.' Fox
looked into the stream where Rabbit pointed, and there
he saw the reflection of the big round yellow moon. He
thought it was a round cheese and he plunged in after it,
for he was very fond of cheese. Rabbit hoped he would
be drowned, but the stream was shallow and Fox climbed
out with no cheese and with only a bad fright and a wet
coat for his pains. He was very cross, for he knew that
Rabbit wished to do him harm, but he kept his anger to
himself.

Rabbit was still eating contentedly.

'What are you eating?' said Fox, trying to hold him in
talk until he could think of a plan to catch him. 'I am
eating good ripe fruit,' said Rabbit; 'I am eating Indian
melons.' 'Throw me one,' said Fox, for he was hungry.
Rabbit threw him a large round wild cucumber all covered with green prickles. 'Swallow it whole at a mouthful,'
said Rabbit. 'It is very good that way.' It was night and
the moon shone dimly through the trees, and Fox could
not see what he was eating. He swallowed the cucumber
at one gulp, as Rabbit had told him, but the prickles
stuck in his throat and he almost choked to death. And
while he was choking and spluttering and trying to cough
up the cucumber, Rabbit ran away as fast as he could,
laughing heartily to himself. Fox knew that he had been
tricked again, and this time he swore he would kill Rab-

bit as soon as he could find him: he resolved that when next he saw him he would not give him a moment to live.

Rabbit hid among the dry underbrush all the next day. But when the day went down and the sky was red in the west and the wind was very still, he sat on a log, as was his custom, and played softly on his flute, for he was a great player on the Indian pipe. While he was playing, Fox suddenly came upon him unawares. Rabbit saw him watching him through the trees close at hand, but, although taken by surprise, he was not to be outdone. Fox was just about to spring upon him when Rabbit said: 'The Chief's daughter has just been married to a great warrior and the wedding party will soon be along this way. They asked me to sit here and make music for them with my flute as they pass by. They have promised to pay me well, and they have invited me to the wedding feast. Come and join me and play too and you will be well paid, and we will go to the wedding feast together and get good things to eat.'

Fox thought he would let Rabbit get the pay he had been promised, for he was a very greedy fellow; then he would rob him and kill him, and he would take his flute and go to the wedding feast alone, and his vengeance would then be complete. So he decided to let his anger cool for a little time, and he said: 'I have no flute, and I cannot therefore make music; but I will sit with you to see the wedding guests go by.' But Rabbit said: 'Take my flute. I have another at home. I will go and get it, for there is yet time.'

So Fox took the flute and began to play loudly, and Rabbit slipped hurriedly out of sight, pretending to go for his Indian pipe. But he resolved to make an end of

Fox, for he feared for his own life, and instead of going home, he set the underbrush on fire. He kindled the fire at many places all around the log on which Fox sat. Fox could not hear the fire crackling because of the loud music of his flute, and he thought the light was but the bright light of the moon. And the fire was almost upon him before he knew that he was in danger. Then he tried to get away, but on all sides his escape was stopped by the flames, and he could not find an opening. At last, in despair, to save his life, he jumped through the ring of fire.

He escaped with his life, but his eyelids were singed, and his sleek black coat with its silver spots was scorched to a red-brown colour. He was in great pain. He concluded that Rabbit was too clever for him to cope with, and he resolved to leave him alone and to forgo his revenge, for he was glad to get away with his life. But he decided never again to live on friendly terms with Rabbit. And since that night Rabbit and Fox have never hunted together. And to the present day the descendants of this Fox have red eyes and a red-brown coat, because Rabbit scorched their ancestor in the olden times.

Rabbit and the Grain Buyers

Once long ago, when the Indians lived in Canada before the white men came, Rabbit was very lazy. He had worked long for Glooskap, the great ruler of the people, as a forest guide, but his toil was not appreciated or rewarded. He saw all the other animals idling their time away, taking their ease all day long, and doing nothing but filling their bellies with food and sleeping all the afternoon in the hot sunshine. And he said: 'Why should I work for other people when nobody works for me? I will take mine ease like all the other animals.' So he sulked in his little house for a long time and could not be coaxed or driven to do any work. But as he was a lonely fellow who always lived by himself with very few friends in the world except little children, he soon got tired of this lazy life. For by nature he was industrious and energetic and he always liked to be doing something or prowling alone in the forest. So he said: 'I must find some work to do or I shall surely lose my wits. But it must be labour that brings profit to myself and not to other people.'

For a long time Rabbit puzzled his brains thinking on a business or a profession to follow. But nothing seemed to be to his liking. At last one day he saw some Indians trading skins and knives. One was selling and others were buying and they seemed to be making a great deal of money without doing very much work. Rabbit thought that here indeed was an easy way to make a living. Then he saw Duck coming along carrying a basket of eggs. He said to Duck: 'How do you get along in the world? You seem to do nothing but eat and cackle and swim in the pond. You never seem to work.' And Duck said: 'I lay eggs and sell them in exchange for corn. Why don't you lay eggs? It is all very easy.' But Rabbit knew that Duck was only laughing at him and that he was not meant to make a living in that way.

Then he met Bee on the forest path and he said: 'How do you make a living, you wandering bee? You do nothing but gad about all day long, going from flower to flower dressed in your good clothes of yellow and black and always singing your tuneless song?' And Bee said: 'I make honey and wax and sell them. I have a great store for sale now. Why don't you do as I do? I am always happy. I always sing at my work, and what's more, my song is not tuneless. And just for your impudence, take that.' And so saying he stung Rabbit on the nose and went on his way, singing his droning song. Rabbit rubbed his nose in the earth to ease his pain and he swore vengeance on Bee, for he knew that Bee too was only laughing at him. But he could think of no way to make an easy living, for he had nothing to sell but his coat, and he could not very well barter that, for winter would soon be coming on.

He was very angry and troubled and he envied Duck and
Bee their good fortune because of their eggs and honey
and wax.

At last he thought of the Indians he had watched
buying and selling skins. 'I have it,' he cried, 'I have it!
I will become a great merchant. I will be a great trader.
I will live on a farm where they grow corn and vegetables, and I will steal them and sell them to the other
animals and thereby make a great store of money. I shall
be very rich in a short time.' So, very happy, he went to
a field near which was a vegetable garden. And in it were
growing Indian corn and all kinds of grains which he
knew the other birds and animals would gladly buy. So
he made a sign and put it up in front of his house, and
it said:

BUY RABBIT'S CORN

THE BEST IN ALL THE LAND

IT WILL GROW WITHOUT RAIN

THERE IS ONLY A SMALL QUANTITY LEFT

ORDERS TAKEN HERE

Then he sat in his house and waited.

Soon many buyers began to arrive. They were curious,
and they wanted to see what kind of a merchant Rabbit
would make. Rabbit explained to them that he was only
an agent, that they must pay him their money and he
would take it to the farmer and deliver their grain at his
house one week from that day. The buyers paid him the
money and went away, for they were afraid the farmer
would kill them if they went themselves for the corn.
They left a great store of money with Rabbit.

That night, when the moon rose over the hills, Rabbit

went to the field of corn near by. But the farmer had
spied him thieving that afternoon, and he had placed
around his corn a fence of strong netting which poor rabbit could not get through. And he had also placed around
the field many watch-dogs which growled and snarled
and frightened thieves away. Night after night Rabbit
tried to slip into the field but without success, and the
week passed and still he had no corn for the customers
who, he knew, would soon be arriving for their goods.
And meanwhile he had spent all their money and he
knew they would all fall upon him and kill him if he
failed to keep his word and deliver their purchases.

At last, when the day agreed on arrived, he saw his
customers coming for their grain, and he hoped that his
tricks would save him as they had saved him many times
before. He sat in his yard playing his flute when Earthworm, the first customer, arrived. 'Good day,' said Rabbit. 'Good day,' said Earthworm. 'I have come for my
corn, for a week has gone by.' 'Very good,' said Rabbit,
'but first we shall have dinner. It will be ready in a few
minutes. You must be hungry after your long journey.'

As they sat waiting for the dinner they saw Duck,
another customer, waddling up the path with her basket
on her neck. And Rabbit said: 'Will not old Duck who
comes here want to eat you up?' And Earthworm said:
'Yes, yes! Where shall I hide?' and he was much excited.
'Hide under this clam-shell,' said Rabbit. So Earthworm
crawled under the clam-shell and sat very still, trembling
for his life.

When Duck arrived, Rabbit said: 'Good morning.'
'Good morning, Mr Merchant,' said Duck, wishing to be
polite. 'I have come for my corn, for it is the appointed

day of delivery.' 'True, true,' said Rabbit, 'but first we shall have dinner. It will be ready in a few minutes. It will be an honour for me to have you dine with me.'

As they sat waiting for the dinner, Rabbit said: 'Would you care to eat an earthworm before your dinner? It would be a good appetizer for you.' And Duck said: 'Thank you very much. I am very fond of earthworms.' Rabbit lifted the clam-shell and poor Earthworm was quickly gobbled up by Duck. And Rabbit, laughing to himself, thought: 'Now I am getting rid of my customers.'

As Rabbit and Duck sat talking, they saw Fox trotting up the path. He was another customer coming for his corn. And Rabbit said courteously: 'Madam, I see your old enemy Fox approaching. He will probably wish to eat you up; you had better hide.' And Duck, with her feathers all ruffled with excitement, said: 'Yes, yes! Where shall I hide?' And Rabbit said: 'Hide under this basket.' So Duck crawled under the over-turned basket and sat very still.

Fox soon came in and said: 'Good day, Rabbit. I have come for my corn, for I am in sore need of it to catch chickens, and the seven days have passed.' 'You are very punctual,' said Rabbit, 'but first let us have dinner. It will be ready in a few minutes. It will make you stronger to carry your heavy load.'

As they sat waiting for their dinner, Rabbit said: 'Listen, Fox. Would you care to eat a fat duck now? It would be a tasty bit for you before you dine.' And Fox said: 'You are very kind. I always like to eat a duck before my dinner.' Rabbit knocked over the basket and Fox quickly devoured poor Duck until not a feather remained. And

Rabbit laughed to himself and said: 'Surely I am getting rid of my customers very easily.'

As Rabbit and Fox sat talking over old times in the forest, they saw Bear coming lumbering up the path, tossing his head from side to side and sniffing the air. And Rabbit said: 'Bear is in a bad temper today. I wonder what can be the cause.' And Fox said: 'This morning I stole all his honey and he saw me running away.' 'He scents you here,' said Rabbit. 'Will he not kill you if he finds you? Perhaps you ought to hide.' 'Yes, yes!' said Fox. 'But where shall I hide?' 'Hide in this box,' said Rabbit, and Fox sprang into the box and Rabbit closed down the lid.

When Bear arrived he said gruffly (for he was in a bad temper) : 'Good day, Rabbit. I have come for my corn and I must have it quickly, for I must be on my way. It is the appointed time.' 'It is indeed the appointed time,' said Rabbit, 'but first we shall have dinner. It will be ready in a few minutes and I never let a wayfarer leave my house without first taking nourishment. I have today a dish of fresh fish which you like very well, and we have never yet dined together.' And Bear agreed to wait, and his gruffness left him at the thought of his good meal, for he was a great fish eater and he talked pleasantly. Then Rabbit said: 'I have a secret to tell you. Let me whisper it.' He put his mouth close to Bear's ear and said: 'Old Fox, the sly thief who stole all your honey this morning, is hiding in the box by your side. He came here to boast about his theft and he laughed loudly to me as he told me how easily you were cheated. He called you Lack-Brains.' Bear was very angry and at once he knocked the lid from the box and killed Fox with one blow of his powerful paw. And Rabbit said to himself: 'What luck I am having! There is another of my customers gone.' But he wondered how he was to get rid of Bear, and he scratched his head in thought.

While Bear and Rabbit sat talking, they saw Rabbit's last customer, the Hunter, coming along. Bear would have run away, but it was too late. 'Will the Hunter not want to kill you?' said Rabbit, glad to think that here was the end of poor Bear. 'Indeed he will,' said Bear. 'Oh, dear! Oh, dear! Where shall I hide?' 'Hide under my bed in my house,' said Rabbit. Poor Bear quickly dashed into the house and crawled under Rabbit's bed with great difficulty, for he was very fat and the bed was very low and he had to lay himself out flat on the floor, but he was comfortable in the thought that he would soon escape.

When Hunter arrived he said: 'Good day, Rabbit. I have

come for my corn, for my children need bread.' 'You shall have it,' said Rabbit. 'But first we must have a bite to eat. I have not very much to offer you, but I can give you in a few minutes some hot pancakes and fresh maple syrup.' The Hunter was well pleased with the thought of such a good meal and he said he would be glad to wait. Then Rabbit said: 'Would you like some bear meat for your children, and a good warm bear skin for your hearth?' And the Hunter said: 'Indeed I would. But in these days such luxuries are hard to find.' And Rabbit said: 'Oh no, they are not; under my bed in my house, a good fat bear is hiding. He is lying flat on his back and you can easily kill him.'

The Hunter hurried to the house, and sure enough, there he found Bear hiding under the bed, flat upon his back. He killed him with a blow and skinned him and cut him up into small pieces and put the meat and the skin into a bag to take home to his children. But while he was about it, Rabbit slipped away into the forest, saying to himself: 'Now I have got rid of all my customers and I am safe. But the life of a merchant is not to my liking. I will not be a trader any more. I will gather corn for my-self, but not sell to others.' And he ran quickly away and hid himself in a dense thicket.

When the Hunter went to look for Rabbit, he could not find him, nor was he able to find his grain. And al-though he thought he had fared pretty well by getting so much bear meat, he swore vengeance on Rabbit for his deceit, and to this day he searches for him, and if he meets him, he will not let him escape. And Rabbit lives by himself and keeps away from the Hunter as far as he can, for he fears him because of the trick he played upon him in the olden days.

Owl with the Great Head and Eyes

Long ago, when Glooskap was the ruler of the Indians in Eastern Canada and when the animals all worked for him and talked like men, Wolf was one of Rabbit's enemies. On the surface they seemed to be friends, but each was afraid of the other and each suspected the other of treachery. Rabbit was very faithful to his work as the forest guide who showed people the way to far places. But he was also a great trickster, and he delighted to play pranks on everyone he met. He liked more than all to pester Wolf, for he had a hatred for his cruel ways, and he was always able to outwit him.

It happened that Rabbit and Wolf lived close together, deep in the Canadian forest. Some distance from them, in a little house, lived a poor widow woman who had only one daughter. She was a very beautiful girl, with hair as black as the raven's wing and with eyes like the dark of the underwater. Rabbit and Wolf each fell in love with her, and each in his own way sought her as his wife. Rabbit tried hard to win her love. When he went to her house he always dressed himself in a soft brown coat, and he put a bangle around his neck and bells upon his feet. And often he played sweetly on his flute, hoping to charm her with his music, for he was a great player upon the Indian pipe. And he tried to grow a moustache to hide his split lip; but he had little success, for his whiskers would not grow thick, and he has the thin scraggy moustache of a few hairs to this day. But no matter what Rabbit did to adorn himself, the girl gave him cold looks, and old Wolf seemed to be deeper in her favour, for she liked his willowy form and his sleek and bashful ways. And poor Rabbit was sore distressed.

One fine day in the springtime Rabbit came upon the girl and her mother gathering May-flowers among the moss. He crept close to listen to their talk. He heard the mother say: 'I have no stomach for little Rabbit, but Wolf pleases me well. You must marry Wolf. They tell me he is a great hunter, and if you marry him we shall never want for food.'

When Rabbit heard this he was very sad; he determined that on no account should Wolf marry the widow's daughter, and that he must use all his power to prevent it. That night he went alone to the girl's house. He spoke sneeringly of Wolf, saying with a bitter frown: 'Wolf is no hunter; he never catches any game because he is lazy and he has no brains; I always have to feed him to keep him from starving. He is but a beast of burden. I always ride upon his back when I go to a far country, for he is good for nothing else.' The girl's mother wondered greatly, and she was very startled by this news, for she did not want her daughter to marry a good-for-nothing; but she was not sure that Rabbit spoke the truth, for she heard that sometimes he told great lies. So she said: 'If you will ride Wolf over here I will believe you, and he shall not marry my daughter, and you shall marry her yourself.' And Rabbit went home well pleased and sure of a happy ending to his trick.

The next day Rabbit purposely met Wolf in the forest, and he said: 'Let us go together to see the widow's daughter.' And Wolf was glad to go. They had not gone far when Rabbit began to cry. Then he lay down on the ground and rolled and moaned and rubbed his belly as if in great distress. 'I have a sharp pain in my belly,' he sobbed. 'I cannot walk any farther. If I walk I shall surely die, and I cannot go unless you carry me on your back.' Wolf willingly agreed, for he wanted to see the beautiful girl and he was very sorry for poor Rabbit in his pain; and Rabbit, laughing to himself, climbed on Wolf's back.

Wolf ran along not feeling the load, for Rabbit was very light. They had not gone far when Rabbit cried again and said: 'I cannot ride without a saddle, for your bare back hurts me and gives me blisters.' So they borrowed a little saddle from a field by the way and put it on Wolf's back. Soon Rabbit said: 'This is fine fun; let us play that you are a horse and that I am a great rider. I should like to put a little bridle on you, and to wear spurs on my feet and to carry a whip.' And Wolf, wishing to please Rabbit to make him forget his pain, gladly agreed. So they borrowed a little bridle and spurs and a whip from another field near by and did as Rabbit asked, and together they went to the girl's home, Wolf trotting along like a little horse, and Rabbit laughing to himself, sitting in the saddle, with

his spurs and his whip, holding the bridle reins.

When they drew near the house, Rabbit made a great noise so that the mother and her daughter might look out to see where the shouting came from. He called loudly: 'Whoa! Whoa!' And the girl and her mother opened the door and looked out at them in wonder. Then, as they were looking on, Rabbit, chuckling to himself, struck Wolf a stinging blow with his whip and stuck his spurs deep into Wolf's sides and called him loudly a lazy beast. Wolf jumped and plunged and kicked because of the prick of the spurs and the sting of the whip; he was very cross, but he said nothing.

Some distance away, Rabbit tied Wolf to a tree, saying: 'Stay here and I will send the girl to you.' Then he went to the house and he said to the woman: 'Now you will believe that Wolf is a beast of burden, for I have ridden here on his back.' And the woman believed him. She told him to give Wolf some corn or grass. But Rabbit said: 'He doesn't eat corn or grass; he eats only fresh meat,' for he knew well that Wolf would be quite contented if he got a good meal of meat. Then she gave him some fresh meat, which he brought to Wolf. And Wolf was happy, and his anger disappeared, and he forgot the pain of the spurs and the whip, and he thought it was fine fun to get a good meal so easily.

The woman promised that Rabbit should marry her daughter, and when night fell Rabbit went home well pleased, leaving Wolf still tied to the tree. It was so dark that Wolf did not see him leaving the house, and for a long time he thought he was still inside, and he waited long in the starlight. At last he grew tired waiting, for he was hungry and he was cold standing still in the chill night air of early spring. He cut with his teeth the bridle rein that tied him to the tree, and then he went to the woman's house. But the woman would not let him in. She told him to go away, that she never wished to see him again, and she called him a lazy beast of burden. He went home in great anger, for he knew now that he had been tricked, and he swore that he would have vengeance on Rabbit.

The next day Rabbit learned from the woman that she had spurned Wolf from her door, and he knew that Wolf realized he had been deceived. He was somewhat frightened, for he dreaded Wolf's vengeance, and for several days he hid among the trees. Then hunger drove him out and he went forth to look for food. One evening he entered a garden in search of cabbage, and he was busy robbing it when the people who owned the garden spied him. And they said: 'Here is the thief who has been stealing our vegetables. We will catch him and teach him a lesson.' Before Rabbit knew it, they were upon him (for he was eating heartily, he was so hungry), and they caught him and bound him fast to a tree and went to get scalding water to pour upon his back to teach him not to rob their garden again.

But while they were away Wolf came along. He, too, was very hungry, for he had eaten no meal for many days, but he was glad when he saw Rabbit, for now he thought he would have his revenge. Rabbit saw him at a distance, and he resolved to try another trick on him, and to hail him as if he thought he was still his friend. And he cried out to him: 'Help me, Wolf! Help me! The people here asked me to eat up a nice little lamb, and when I refused to do it, they tied me up to this tree and they have gone to bring the lamb to me.'

Wolf was too hungry to be cautious and he forgot all about Rabbit's tricks, for spring lamb was his favourite food. And he said: 'I will eat up the little lamb,' and he smacked his lips as he spoke, and thought of the nice tender meal he would have. Then Rabbit said: 'Untie me and take my place, for the people will soon be here with the lamb.' So Wolf untied him, and Rabbit in turn bound Wolf fast to the tree and, laughing to himself because he had again outwitted stupid Wolf, he ran rapidly away. Far off he hid behind the trees to see what would happen.

Soon the people came back, carrying the pots of scalding water. Wolf saw them coming, and he was in high spirits, for he thought the lamb he was to eat was in one of the pots. It was moonlight, and in the shadow of the great tree the people could not see very clearly and they thought Wolf was Rabbit, still bound fast where they had left him. So they poured the scalding water on his back and kicked him and knocked him on the head with a big stick, and they said: 'Now, thief, we have taught you how dangerous it is to rob gardens in the spring moonlight.' Wolf howled with pain, for his back was blistered and his head was sore, and Rabbit heard him, and he sat on a log and shook with laughter because of the success of his prank.

Then the people untied Wolf and let him go. He went away wearily among the trees. And he again swore vengeance on Rabbit, and he resolved to kill him as soon as he set eyes upon him, for he knew he had been tricked a second time. For several days he searched for his enemy. At last, one night of bright moonlight, he came upon Rabbit sitting in a patch of Indian tobacco plants eating his fill and contentedly chewing the tobacco leaves. Rabbit's mouth was full of tobacco, but he laughed loudly when he saw Wolf's back bound in bandages because of the blisters, and his sore head tied up in a cloth. But when he saw Wolf's angry eyes he was frightened and he ran away into the woods. The moon was shining in the forest and Wolf could catch a glimpse now and then of his brown coat among the trees, and he chased him for a long time. Rabbit tried all his tricks to shake him from his tracks, but without avail.

At last, when Rabbit was almost worn out, he took refuge in a hollow tree into which he slipped through a small hole where Wolf could not follow him. And Wolf said: 'Now I have him in my power. I will kill him; but first I must go home to get my axe to cut down the tree and to chop off his head.' Then he looked around for someone to keep watch over the tree while he was gone so that Rabbit could not escape. At last he saw Owl sitting quietly on a branch near by. He called to him and said: 'Watch by this hole until I get back, and do not let Rabbit get away.' So Owl came down and sat by the hole and promised to keep guard over the prisoner, and Wolf went away to look for his axe.

But Rabbit was not caught yet; he had another trick left. After Wolf had gone away, he called to Owl sitting by the hole and said: 'Owl, come and see what a nice little room I have here in the tree.' But Owl replied: 'It is too dark, I cannot see.' Then Rabbit said: 'Open your eyes wide and put your face close to the hole, for I have a light here and you can see easily.' Owl did as he was told, for he was a curious fellow. Rabbit had a great mouthful of tobacco juice from the Indian tobacco leaves he had been chewing, and when Owl put his face close to the hole, he squirted the juice into Owl's eyes. Owl screamed loudly, for his eyes were smarting and he was blinded by the juice; he ran around the tree and stamped and shrieked and rubbed his eyes, trying to relieve them of their pain. And while he was about it, Rabbit slipped out of the hole and ran away, and Owl did not know he was gone.

Soon Wolf came back, carrying his big sharp axe. And he said: 'Now I shall kill him at last.' And Owl was afraid to tell him about his sore eyes; they were still open wide and he could not close them. At once Wolf chopped down the hollow tree. Then he split it open from end to end, but there was no sign of Rabbit. Wolf then thought Owl had tricked him and that he had helped Rabbit to escape. But Owl said he had not. He sat with his eyes wide open, staring stupidly and moaning and making strange noises because of his pain. Wolf thought he was laughing at him and taunting him, for he did not know the meaning of

Owl's strange cries, and in his rage he fell to beating him over the head with his axe-handle until poor Owl's head was swollen to a great size. And Owl cried: 'Hoot, hoot, hoot!' and his eyes stared from his swollen head even larger than before.

Then Wolf went on his way, resolved to keep away from Rabbit. And since that time Owl has cried 'Hoot, hoot, hoot!' at night, for he still remembers his pain; and his head is still swollen and bigger than that of other birds because of the beating Wolf gave him with his axe-handle; and his eyes are still large and they stare stupidly, and he cannot look at light, and he is blind in the daylight because of the tobacco juice Rabbit squirted into his eyes. And since that night Rabbit and Wolf have avoided each other, and they have not lived in the same place, and they have never since been friends.

Rabbit and the Moon-Man

Once long ago, Rabbit lived with his old grandmother deep in the Canadian forest, far from all other people. He was a great hunter, and all around, far and near, he laid snares and set traps to catch game for food. It was winter, and he caught many little animals and birds. He brought them home daily to feed himself and his old grandmother, and he was well pleased with his success. But after some weeks had passed he was unable to catch any game. He always found his traps and snares empty, although many tracks were always around them, and there were many signs that animals were prowling about. He knew then that he was being robbed nightly, and that a thief was pilfering his traps. It was very cold and the snow lay deep in the forest, and Rabbit and his old grandmother were in dire need of food. Every morning Rabbit rose very early and hurried off to his traps, but always he found them empty, for the thief had been ahead of him.

He was greatly puzzled, for he could not think who the thief was.

At last one morning, after a new fall of snow, he found the mark of a long foot near his traps, and he knew it was the foot of the game-robber. It was the longest footprint he had ever seen, long and narrow and very light, like a moonbeam. And Rabbit said: 'Now I shall rise earlier in the morning, and I shall go to my traps ahead of the thief and take my game so that they will all be empty when he comes.' Each morning he rose earlier to catch the thief, but the man of the long foot was always there before him, and his game was always gone. No matter how early Rabbit got up, the thief was always ahead of him and his traps were always empty.

So Rabbit said to his old grandmother: 'The man of the long foot who robs my traps is always up ahead of me no matter how early I rise. I will make a snare from a bow-string and I will watch all this night, and I will surely catch him.' He made a trap from a stout bow-string and set it beside his snares and took the end of the bow-string some distance away to a clump of trees, behind which he hid. He hoped that the thief would step into the trap; then he would pull the bow-string and tie him fast to a tree.

He sat very quiet, waiting for the man of the long foot to appear. It was moonlight when he set out, but soon it grew very dark in the forest. The moon suddenly disappeared. But the stars were all shining on the white snow and there were no clouds in the sky, and Rabbit wondered what had happened to the moon. He waited very still and a little frightened in the starlight.

Soon he heard someone coming, sneaking stealthily

through the trees. Then he saw a white light which dazzled his eyes. The light went towards the snares until it stopped just at the trap Rabbit had set. Then Rabbit pulled the bow-string, closed the trap as he had hoped, and tied the string fast to a tree. He heard sounds of a struggle and he saw the white light move from side to side, but he knew that he had his prisoner fast and that the man of the long foot was caught at last. He was much afraid of the white light, and he ran home as fast as he could and told his old grandmother that he did not know who he was, for he was too frightened to look. And his grandmother said: 'You must go back and see who it is, and tell him he must stop robbing your snares.' But Rabbit said: 'I do not want to go until daylight, for the Moon has gone down and the forest is very dark.' But his grandmother said: 'You must go.' So poor Rabbit, although he was very frightened by what he had seen, set out again for his traps.

When he drew near to his snares he saw that the white light was still shining. It was so bright that his eyes were dazzled and he had to stop far from it. Then he approached nearer, but his eyes soon became very sore. There was a stream flowing beside him, and he bathed his eyes in the cold water, but it brought him no relief, and his eyes felt hot and red, and tears fell from them because of the dazzling light. Then he took great handfuls of snow and threw snowballs at the light, hoping thereby to put it out. But when the snowballs came near to the light they melted and fell down like rain. Then, with his eyes still smarting, Rabbit in his rage scooped up great handfuls of soft black mud from the bottom of the stream and, forming it into balls, he threw them with all his force at the white light. He heard them strike something with a dull thud, and he heard loud yells from the prisoner—the man of the long foot—behind the shining light. Then a voice came from the light, saying: 'Why did you snare me? Come and untie me at once. I am the Man in the Moon. It is near the morning, and before dawn I must be on my way home. You have already spotted my face with mud, and if you do not loose me at once I shall kill all your tribe.'

Poor Rabbit was more frightened than before, and he ran home and told his grandmother what had happened. And his grandmother was also very frightened, for she thought that no good could come of it. And she told Rabbit to go back at once and untie the Man of the Moon, for the night was almost spent and the dawn would soon be breaking. So poor Rabbit, trembling in his fear, went back to his traps. From a great distance he cried: 'I will untie you if you will never again rob my snares and if you will never come back to earth.' And the prisoner in the trap promised, and said: 'I swear it by my white light.' Then Rabbit approached very carefully. He had to shut his eyes and grope his way because of the bright light, and his lip quivered because of the great heat. At last he rushed in and cut the bow-string snare with his teeth, and the Man in the Moon hurried on his way, for he could already see the dawn in the east. But Rabbit was almost blinded while he was about it, and his shoulders were badly scorched. And ever since that time Rabbit blinks and his eyelids are pink, and water runs from his eyes when he looks at a bright light; and his lip always quivers; and his shoulders are yellow, even when he wears his white winter coat, because of the great light and heat on the winter night long ago when he loosed the Man in the Moon from the snare.

And since that night the Man in the Moon has never come back to earth. He stays at his task in the sky, lighting the forest by night; but he still bears on his face the marks of the black mud which Rabbit threw at him. And sometimes for several nights he goes away to a quiet place where he tries to wash off the mud, and then the land is dark. But he never succeeds in cleaning himself, and when he comes back to his work the marks of Rabbit's mud-balls are still upon his shining face.

Rabbit and the Indian Chief

Long ago an Indian Chief was living with his people far in the Canadian forest. Life was good and food was plentiful and the people were all very happy. But one day a wicked giant and his old witch-wife came crashing into the land from a far country beyond the prairies. They devoured all the food they could lay their hands on and soon there was little left to eat in all the country; and often they carried off little children to their hiding-place and ate them up until not a trace of them remained. Somewhere far in the forest they dwelt in a hidden cave; they slept all day long, but at night they always stalked forth in search of plunder. The Chief was much troubled, and with his warriors he tried in every way to discover their hiding-place, but no one ever succeeded in finding it. For by the use of their magic power the giant and his old witch-wife could make themselves invisible when they walked abroad among men, and they could not be caught. The Chief called all his warriors to a council, and he said: 'Who can rid me of this pest? Who can kill the giant?' But not a man replied. And when he saw his people's store of food rapidly growing smaller and the little children of his tribe slowly disappearing, he was greatly puzzled as to what he should do.

One night of bright moonlight Rabbit was prowling through the woods, as was his custom, in search of someone on whom he could play a prank, for he was a great joker. Suddenly he came upon the giant and his old witch-wife standing by an opening in the side of a low mountain. He watched them for a long time from the shadow of a great tree, and at last he saw them enter a large hole in the side of the hill. He knew now that he had hit by accident upon the giants' cave, and he was well pleased by his discovery. But he kept his secret to himself, for he thought: 'Here is a good chance for me to win fame. I will kill the giants by a crafty trick and I will then be looked upon as a great warrior, the foremost in all the land, for all the Chief's men have failed to find the giants.'

So he went to the Chief and said: 'Oh, Chief, I know where the giants live and I swear to you that I am going to kill them. It is I alone who can rid you of these pests.'

'You!' said the Chief in great surprise. 'Little harm the like of you can do to the giants; they will eat you up in one mouthful,' and he laughed loudly at Rabbit's boldness. And he called to his warriors, saying: 'See what a stout fighter we have here! Little Rabbit says he can do what we have failed to do; he swears that he will kill the giant. He is better fitted to kill a mouse!' And they all laughed loud haw-haws at Rabbit's vanity.

Poor Rabbit's pride was deeply hurt by the Chief's

scorn and the warriors' cruel laughter, but it all made him more determined than ever to slay the thieving giants, so he went to an old woman who lived near by and said: 'Give me an old faded dress and a ragged old shawl and your coloured spectacles and a hat with a feather in it.' The old woman wondered what tricks he was up to now, but she gave him what he asked for. He put on the tattered old dress and the battered old hat with a red feather sticking from the top, and he wrapped the old shawl about his face, and he wore the woman's coloured spectacles, and he carried a crooked stick. And dressed in this fashion he set out towards evening for the giants' home. When he reached the mouth of the cave, he stood still and waited, leaning on his crooked stick, for night was coming on and he knew that the giants would soon be going out on their plundering rounds.

After a time, when it was quite dark except for the moonlight, the giant's old witch-wife came out of the cave. When she saw Rabbit in the dim light she said gruffly: 'Who are you, standing there in the shadows?'

'Oh, my dear niece,' said Rabbit, 'I have found you at last. I am your poor old aunt. I thought I had lost my way. I have come to see you from your home in the far country. It was a long journey and my poor old legs and back are stiff and sore, and I am very hungry and tired,' and he moved slowly towards the woman, hobbling along with his crooked stick. The giant woman was deceived, and she threw her arms around Rabbit and kissed him, and she did not feel his whiskers or his split lip because of the old shawl that was wrapped around his face. 'I have a pain in my jaw from sleeping out of doors,' said Rabbit, 'and I must keep my face wrapped up.'

'Come in and rest, and you will soon feel better,' said the giant woman.

'You will have to lead me in,' said Rabbit, not wishing to take off the shawl, 'for my eyesight is very bad.'

So she led Rabbit into the warm cave, which was so dark that they could scarcely see each other, and she called her husband and said: 'Here is my dear old aunt who has come all the way from the far country beyond the prairies.' And the giant, believing Rabbit to be his wife's kindred, for he could not see him very clearly, treated him very kindly. And they showed him the bed where he was to sleep.

The woman then gave Rabbit a large piece of dried meat to eat. But Rabbit said: 'I cannot eat it, for I am old and I have lost all my teeth. Give me an axe to cut it up small.' So the woman brought him a sharp axe and he chopped the meat into small pieces and ate it all up. And he said: 'I will keep the axe by me, for I shall need it at all my meals,' and he placed it beside his bed. The giant said: 'We are going away to see some friends, but we shall be back before midnight.' But before they went away, Rabbit said to the woman: 'I hope your husband sleeps soundly. I have a bad cough and I sometimes moan because of the pain in my face and head and I do not wish to disturb him.' And the old giant woman answered: 'He slumbers too well. When we sleep we both snore loudly, and when you hear us snoring you may cough as much as you please, for then you will know that we are sound asleep.' Then the man and his witch-wife went away.

When the giants came home, Rabbit pretended to be fast asleep. They brought back with them much food which they hid in a secret place at the side of the cave.

Rabbit watched them through the holes in the old shawl around his head. Soon they went to bed, drowsy after their fat meal. When Rabbit heard them snoring loudly like a great water-fall ('chr-r-r, chr-r-r'), he arose very quietly and crept softly to their bedside. With two blows of his axe he killed the giant and his wife, one after the other. Then he ran away as fast as he could carrying with him his old dress and hat and shawl, for he thought he might need them again.

In the morning he went to the Chief's house and told the Chief what he had done. The Chief laughed scornfully and he would not believe it until Rabbit brought him to the cave and showed him the slain giants, cold and stiff in their bed. The Chief's men then took back to the village the great store of food the giants had hidden in the secret place. But the Chief and his warriors, although they were glad to be rid of the thieves, were angry at heart because Rabbit, whom they had laughed at, had done what they had failed to do, for they were very jealous of Rabbit's power.

One day soon afterwards the Chief called all the birds and the animals to a council, and he said: 'Now that the giants who robbed us of our food are dead and gone, and that we shall never again want for nourishment in my country, I am going to let each animal and bird choose the kind of food he would most like to live on if he could get it. And they shall never want for that kind of food if it can be provided.' And he called on each to make the choice. And the birds said, 'Grain and seeds and worms,' and the squirrel said, 'Nuts,' and the fox said, 'Chickens,' and the cat said, 'Milk,' and the dog said, 'Meat and bones,' and the weasel said, 'Eggs,' and the wolf said,

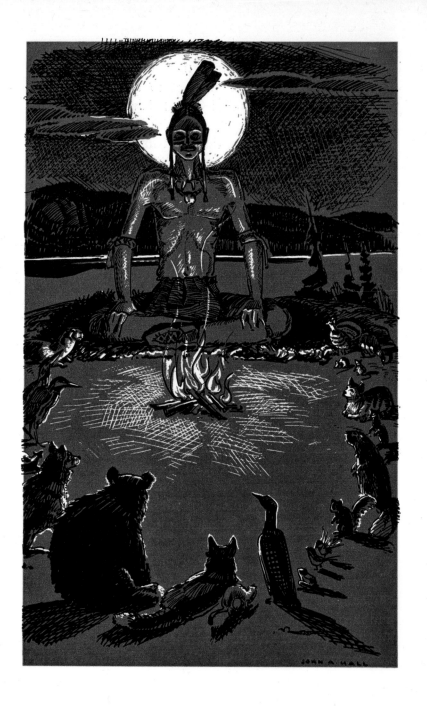

'Lambs,' and the bear said, 'Fish from the frozen sea,' and so on, until each animal was called upon and declared his liking. And the Chief said: 'It shall be as you have chosen.'

But the Chief had purposely neglected to summon poor Rabbit to the council, and Rabbit was absent on a long journey. When he came home, he was very angry when he heard what had happened, for only the left-over in the world's food remained for him to choose. So he went to the Chief and said in great wrath: 'This is a fine return for ridding your land of giants. But that is a way you have—you always reward good deeds with evil.'

The Chief was very angry because of Rabbit's insolence, and he said: 'You are telling lies again.' But Rabbit called as witnesses to the truth of what he said Sheep and Goat and Duck who chanced to be passing by and who stood listening to the quarrel. And old Sheep said: 'Rabbit has spoken truly. When I was young I gave the Chief much wool to make clothes for his back and he used me well. But now that I am old he is going to kill me and eat me up. That is *my* reward.' And old Goat said: 'Rabbit has spoken wisely and justly. I served the Chief well in my time and gave him milk, but now that I am old and have no more milk he is fattening me and getting me ready for slaughter. That is *my* reward.' And old Duck said: 'That is a true saying of Rabbit. Once upon a time I gave the Chief many eggs and young ducklings, but now that I have stopped laying he is soon going to roast me in a pot. That is *my* reward.' The Chief could make no answer to these charges, for he knew them to be true, and he offered to do what was in his power for Rabbit. But Rabbit refused to make choice of food, for he said the best was already gone. He sulked for many months and lived alone by his own efforts as best he could.

At last he decided to take vengeance on the Chief, and he hit, as was his custom, on a crafty trick. The Chief had an old bear which he prized very highly, for the bear did for him many wondrous tricks and brought laughter to him and his warriors when he danced at their feasts. In those olden times Bear had a long bushy tail of which he was very proud. One day, as Rabbit sat on the ice fishing (for it was now winter), Bear came along. There was to be a feast that night, and he was going to dance for the Chief and he was in very good spirits. 'Where did you get all the fine fish?' he asked, for he was a great fish eater. 'I caught them through the hole in the ice,' said Rabbit. 'It is very easy. Just drop your tail down through the hole and it will soon be covered with fine big fish.'

Bear did as he was told, and he sat on the ice for a long time waiting for his prey. He sat so long that the hole froze up, for it was very cold, and in it was frozen poor Bear's long bushy tail. 'Now,' said Rabbit, 'jump quick, for many fish are hanging to you.' Bear jumped with all his might, but his tail was held fast in the ice and it broke off close to the root. Rabbit laughed in great glee and ran away, and poor bear howled with pain and shame. He could not dance at the feast because his stub of a tail was sore, and the Chief and the warriors were very angry at Rabbit because he had harmed their dancing pet. And since that time Bear has had a short stubby tail which to this day he tries to wag feebly.

Rabbit then hid for some days far from the Chief and his warriors. Then he decided to try another trick. The Chief's wood-cutter was old Beaver, who lived in a little house of reeds on the bank of a stream. He was very busy now, cutting down the trees for the Chief, for it was near to springtime and the people were in need of logs for building roads over the rivers. One day Rabbit went to Beaver and said: 'The Chief sent me to you to bring you to a great tree he wishes you to cut down at once.' So Beaver went along with him. But when Beaver was busy at his task cutting down the tree, Rabbit hit him a savage blow on the head with a big stick hoping to kill him and thus again to anger the Chief. Poor Beaver fell to the ground and Rabbit ran away.

But Beaver was only stunned. He got up after a time and went home muttering to himself and rubbing his sore head. Soon Rabbit came back to the tree and found Beaver gone. He knew that his blow had failed. Then he put on again his tattered old dress and his ragged shawl and his coloured spectacles and the hat with the red feather sticking to the top, and he went to Beaver's house by the stream, hobbling along with a stick.

'The Chief sent me to you to bring you to a great tree he wishes you to cut down at once,' he called.

And Beaver said: 'I have already tried to cut a great tree for him today, and I should have finished it had I not been beaten with a stick until I was stunned by the blow.'

'Who struck you?' asked Rabbit, laughing to himself.

'Rabbit struck me,' answered Beaver.

'He is a great brigand and a liar and a thief,' said Rabbit.

'He is all that,' said Beaver, rubbing the lump on his head.

So the Beaver went along with Rabbit. And Rabbit

asked as they went along: 'How is it that you are alive after that cruel blow?'

And Beaver said: 'Rabbit hit me on the head. If he had hit me on the back of my neck he would have killed me, for there I keep the secret of my life.'

When Beaver was busy again at his task, cutting down the tree, Rabbit hit him a powerful blow on the back of the neck and poor Beaver fell down dead. Then he cut off his tail that was made like a file and went away happy, for he knew that the Chief would be very angry when he found what had happened to his wood-cutter.

When the Chief learned that Beaver had been killed, his wrath knew no bounds, for he could ill afford at this time to lose his best wood-chopper. He blamed Rabbit for the deed, but he could not be sure that his suspicions were well founded.

Rabbit kept out of the Chief's sight for some weeks. But one day in early summer he was very hungry. He saw all the other animals filling their bellies with their favourite food, and he decided to forget his sulks and to ask the Chief for help. So he went to the Chief and said haughtily: 'I want you to give me food for my own special use as you have done with the other animals. You must do it at once or I will do you much harm.' Then the Chief remembered what Rabbit had done to his dancing Bear, and he thought of the death of Beaver, for which he blamed Rabbit without proof, and he grew red with anger. He seized Rabbit by the heels and said: 'Henceforth the dogs will always chase you, and you will never have peace when they are near. And you will live for the most part on whatever food I throw you into now.' Then he whirled Rabbit around his head by the heels, and he threw him from him with great force, hoping to drop him in a great black swamp near by. Poor Rabbit went flying through the air for a great distance, farther than the Chief had hoped, and he dropped with a thud into a field of clover on the edge of which cabbages and lettuce were growing.

And since that time the dogs have always chased Rabbit, and he has lived for the most part on cabbages and lettuce and clover, which he steals on moonlight nights from farmers' fields.

The Moon and His Frog-wife

When Glooskap first reigned upon the earth, what is now the Moon shone by day and what is now the Sun shone by night. Their work was exactly opposite to what it is today, for the present Moon was then the Sun and the present Sun was then the Moon. The Moon was then very red and bright; the Sun was pale and silvery. At that time the Sun—the present Moon—kept very irregular hours and was very careless about his work. Sometimes he rose very early in the morning and set very late at night; at other times he rose very late and went to bed very early. For weeks in the winter he refused to shine at all, and even when he did appear at his work he gave very little warmth and he might just as well have been covered in his clouds. The Moon—the present Sun—was, on the other hand, always faithful to his duties.

At last the people grew tired of the Sun's strange actions and irregularities. They protested loudly against his methods of work, until in the end they sent some of their number to complain to Glooskap. Glooskap rebuked the Sun, but the latter answered that he had done his work as well as he could, and that his accusers were merely his enemies. Glooskap had really been too busy to notice the Sun's way of working; so, that he might treat all with fairness, he said to the accusers: 'Charge the Sun formally and openly with neglect of his duty. I will call a great meeting of all my people; we will hold a trial to judge him. I myself will be the judge; whoever wants to give evidence may do so, and the Sun may make his defence.' To this all the people and the Sun agreed.

Now in those days the Sun had many wives. With some of them he was far from happy, for often they sorely tormented him and tried his patience, and a few of them he would gladly get rid of if he could. One of his scolding wives was Frog. She had a crumpled back and a wrinkled face and a harsh voice; she was always jumping about, and with her of all his wives he was on the least friendly terms. When she heard that her husband was to be tried before Glooskap on a serious charge, she wished to be present at the trial, for she was very inquisitive. But the Sun said: 'This trial is for men, not for women. Your place is at home and not in the courts of warriors; you must not come.' The Frog-wife pleaded to be allowed to go, but the more she pleaded the more sternly the Sun refused his permission. However, being a woman, and not to be outdone by a man, she resolved to go to the trial whether her husband permitted it or not, and she decided to steal into the court quietly after the trial had commenced.

At last the day of the trial arrived. The great court-tent was filled with Glooskap's people. In the centre of

the platform sat Glooskap, and near him sat the Sun,
eager to defend himself from the charges of his enemies.
When the trial was well advanced, and the evidence had
nearly all been taken, the Sun's Frog-wife appeared suddenly at the door. All the seats were filled, but Glooskap
with his usual politeness arose to find her a place. But
when the Sun saw her there contrary to his wishes, he was
very angry. He looked at her sternly with a frown, making at her a wry, twisted face; and drawing down his
right eyelid, he said to Glooskap: 'Oh, Master, do not
trouble yourself to find her a seat. Let her sit on my eyelid. That is a good enough seat for her; she can hang
there well enough, for she always wants to stick to me and
follow me wherever I go.' And at once the Frog-wife
jumped to his eyelid and sat there quite comfortably.

Then the trial went on. Because of the Sun's clever
defence of himself he was declared 'not guilty' of the
charges against him. It was decided by the judge, Glooskap—and all the people, even the accusers, agreed—that
under the circumstances he had done his work as well as
he could and that he deserved neither blame nor punishment. But at the close of the trial, when the Sun attempted to go back to his work, he could not get rid of
his Frog-wife. He tried with all his might but he could
not shake her off. She stuck fast to his eyelid and stubbornly refused to leave her seat, and she said that henceforth she would stay with him to see that he did his work
well. All the people pulled and tugged and coaxed, but
they failed to move her. The strongest men in the land
came, but even they could not pull her away. Then the
people lamented and said to Glooskap: 'She covers the
side of the Sun's face and hinders his work. She makes

him ugly. We must not have our Light of Day disfigured like this and bright on one side only; all the world will laugh at us. What are we to do?' And they were in great sorrow and distress.

But Glooskap in his wisdom found a way out of the difficulty. He said: 'Be not troubled, O my people! We will make the Moon and the Sun change places; the Moon, who is still perfect and unharmed, shall become the Light of Day instead of Night, and shall take the name Sun. The Sun shall become the Light of Night instead of Day, and shall take the name Moon, for at night it will matter little if one side of his face is dark, and his Frog-wife hanging to his eyelid will by night be little noticed.' To this the people all agreed. And so the Sun was changed with the Moon to shine by night, and the Moon was changed with the Sun to shine by day.

So now when the Moon—the old Sun—first appears at his work, he holds away from the earth the side of his face to which his Frog-wife is hanging, for he is very much ashamed of his appearance. And when he turns his head full upon the earth, you can still see, when the sky is clear, his black Frog-wife hanging to his right eyelid and covering one side of his face. And always when his month's work is nearly done he turns his head abruptly in a frantic effort to shake her off, but he never succeeds. She hangs there always, and because of his Frog-wife's curiosity he shall never shine again by day.

The First Pig and Porcupine

A man and his wife lived once long ago in the Canadian forest. They lived far away from other people and they found it very lonely. They were very poor, for game was not plentiful, yet they were always happy and contented. They had only one child, a boy, whom they loved well. The boy grew up to be very strong and clever. But he was often lonely without any companions but his parents. The birds and the animals of the woods were his friends because he was kind to them and they looked upon him as a comrade.

At last he grew tired of his lonely life. He longed for adventure. So one day he said to his parents: 'I am going far away to see other men and women and to do great deeds.' His parents did not want to let him go at first, for they would be very lonely without him. But they knew that he could never become great where he was, and they consented to let him go.

The next morning he set out on his journey. He travelled all day. At night he slept on the ground under the stars. In the morning Rabbit came to where he lay and woke him up.

Rabbit said: 'Hello, friend. Where are you going?'

'I am going to find people,' said the boy.

'That is what I want to do too,' said Rabbit. 'We shall go together.' So they went on together.

They travelled a long distance through the forest; they crossed many small streams and climbed many hills. At last they heard voices through the trees, and soon they saw not far in front of them an Indian village. Rabbit hid among the trees, but the boy went forward alone to see the people. The people were all kind to him and gave him food and asked him to stay with them. But they were all very sad and many of them were weeping. 'The Chief has a very beautiful daughter, and word has come to us that tomorrow a great giant is coming to eat her up. It will be useless to send her away, for the giant will follow her. He is a very terrible monster and cannot be killed.' Then they continued to weep and lament.

The boy went out to the woods and told Rabbit what he had heard. He said: 'We had better go on our way so that we may be far off when the giant comes.' But Rabbit said: 'No. Go back to the people and tell them you can save the Chief's daughter. Have no fear. When night comes, bring the girl to me and I will save her.'

So the boy went back to the people and told them not to fear, for he would save the girl from the giant. They laughed at him at first, for everyone who had attempted to stop the giant had been killed. But when they saw that the boy was quite sure of his power, they listened to him. They went to the Chief and told him what the stranger had said. Then the Chief sent for him and said: 'If you can save my daughter from the giant, she shall be yours.'

When evening came, the boy brought the girl to where Rabbit was waiting. Rabbit had a little carriage ready, drawn by two little squirrels. When he spoke to the squirrels they grew until they were as large as dogs. They all got into the carriage, the boy and the girl and Rabbit, and away went the squirrels.

It was a clear summer night and the moon was full. The road was hard, and they ran along rapidly over the road among the trees, and soon they reached a village far away. They came to a tent on the bank of a stream. The boy went in and found only an old woman. She said: 'Death is not far away from you. The giant is close on your heels.' Then she wept. She told them to go to the river, for her husband was there. So they went to the river. Rabbit and his squirrels stayed behind to see what the giant would do. The boy and girl found an old man fishing from the bank. He said: 'Death is not far away from you, for the giant is close on your tracks. But I will help you.' He sprang into the water and lay there and spread out his arms and legs. Then he said: 'Stand on my back.' So they stepped to his back. They feared at first that they would fall off; but at once he grew as large as a big canoe, and he swam with them across the river. When they landed on the other side they turned to look at him and they saw then that he was old Sea Duck, the boy's friend. He pointed to a high mountain. 'Go to the mountain,' he said, 'and there you will find Rabbit.' Then he swam away.

The boy and the girl went towards the mountain. But they heard the giant roaring behind them and splashing in the stream as he crossed. When they reached the foot of the mountain, he was almost upon them. At the foot of the mountain Rabbit was waiting for them. The side of the mountain was very steep—it was almost perpendicular. Rabbit took a long pole and held it up. 'Climb this,' he said. As the boy and the girl climbed, the pole lengthened until they stepped from it to the top of the mountain. Rabbit climbed up after them with his squirrels. The giant saw them all from the foot of the mountain and climbed up the pole after them. But when he was near the top, the boy pushed the pole out and it fell backwards, taking the giant with it. The giant was killed by the fall.

Then the boy and the girl and Rabbit got into the squirrel carriage. They went quickly down the other side of the mountain and over the moonlit road until they came to the girl's native village. When they reached the border of the village, Rabbit said: 'Now, old friend, goodbye. I must go away. But if ever again you are in trouble, I will help you if I can.' Then Rabbit and his squirrels went away.

The boy brought the girl back to the Chief's home. The people all wondered greatly to see her alive. The Chief said to the boy: 'You may have her as your wife.' So they were married and a great wedding feast was held.

But two young men of the girl's village were very angry because the girl had married a stranger. Each wanted her for himself. So they decided to kill her husband. They asked him to go fishing with them far out to sea. The next day the boy went with them to the deep-sea fishing place. It was a long sail. When they were almost out of sight of land, the boy's enemies threw him over-

board before he could defend himself and sailed away, leaving him struggling in the water. The boy called for help. Not far away was a small island, and from the beach came a large white sea-gull in answer to his cries. When Sea-gull saw his plight, he said: 'Have no fear, old friend, I will help you.' Sea-gull flew away and the boy lay on his back and floated with the tide. Soon Sea-gull came back carrying a long cord. He let down one end of it and told the boy to hold on to it tight. Then he said: 'It is a long swim to the island, but I will tow you there.' And Sea-gull towed him to the island and left him there, saying: 'I am very tired after such a long pull. I can go no farther. Goodbye, old friend. Others will help you.'

As the boy sat shivering on the island beach, Fox came along.

'Hello, old friend,' said Fox. 'What are you doing here?' The boy told him what had happened, and said: 'I am very hungry.' Fox said: 'I have no food for you, but I can help you in another way.' Then Fox picked a blade of grass from the bank and said: 'Eat it.' The boy ate it and at once he was changed into a horse and ate grass until he was full and his hunger had left him. When Fox saw that he was full, he gave him another blade of grass,

and said: 'Eat it.' He ate it and at once he was changed
back to a boy. Then Fox said: 'When night comes, I will
take you home, for there is no boat on the island.' So they
waited for the evening. When night came and the moon
came out, they went to the water's edge. They could see
the lights of the village far away across the sea. 'Catch
hold of my tail,' said Fox, 'and hang on tight.' The boy
caught Fox's tail and Fox swam away towing the boy behind him. The sea was very rough, and the waves ran
high, and the boy thought he would never reach the
land. But he held on tight and after some hours they came
to the shore. Fox said: 'Goodbye, old friend. I must go no
farther. But if you are ever again in trouble, call me and
I will help you.' Then Fox ran away along the beach.

The boy made a fire and dried his clothes and then
went to the village. The people all wondered greatly to
see him alive. They thought he was dead. They said:
'Tomorrow one of the men who took you fishing is to
marry your wife. He told her you had drowned yourself
because you were sorry you had married her. Then he
asked her to be his wife and she consented.'

The boy went to his old home and there found his
wife. She was very frightened when she saw him, for she
thought he had come back from the land of the dead. He

told her of the treachery of the two men. She wept, but he said: 'Do not weep, but rejoice, for I shall punish the two men tomorrow. There will be no wedding feast for them as they expected.'

The next morning the boy went to the Chief, his father-in-law, and told him what had happened. The Chief said: 'Put the two men to death.' But the boy said: 'No, I have a better form of punishment.' Then he called Fox. When Fox came, he said to him: 'Bring me two blades of grass that can change men into beasts, such as you used to change me yesterday.' Fox ran away and soon came back with the grass. The boy took the two blades, and went to the men who had tried to drown him. He said: 'Here is some sweet grass I found under the sea. Taste it.' And each took a blade and ate it. At once they were changed. One became a pig and the other became a porcupine, and both had coarse hair or bristles all over them, and they had noses of a strange and funny shape. The boy's punishment of his enemies was then complete. He said: 'Live now despised by men, with your noses always to the ground.' So the first pig and the first porcupine appeared upon the earth.

Sparrow's Search for Rain

Long ago, in a village near the sea, many Indian people were living. Among them was a very nice old warrior who had been given great power at his birth, and who therefore could do many wonderful deeds. There was nothing that was beyond his understanding, for he knew all things. His wife had long been dead, but he had one daughter. She was very beautiful and gentle, and she was as nearly perfect as any woman could be. She took no interest in frivolous things and she lived a very quiet life, but all the people liked her well, and she was always welcome wherever she went. Her old father was very proud of her, and he said boastfully: 'She has inherited much of my wisdom, and some day she will marry a great man.' But the girl on her part had little thought of marriage or of men, for she said they had small minds, and she would rather live alone than listen always to their boastfulness and their foolish chatter.

Soon the daughter's fame spread far and wide through

the sea-coast villages, and many suitors came seeking for her hand. But her father said: 'I have nothing to say. She will make her own choice; she must please herself. For today children please themselves and not their parents.' And she said: 'I will marry only someone who can amuse me and interest me and keep me company. I have scant liking for dull people.'

One day Loon came to see her. He was very good-looking, although he was somewhat tall and skinny, and his neck was a bit longer and more scrawny than ordinary, but he wore good clothes and he had great skill as a fisherman. He came because he thought he was very handsome, and he believed that his good looks would win the maiden. But she had no love for Loon, for he had not a word to say. When she talked to him he only stared and at last he burst out into loud and foolish laughter. Then the maiden said: 'You have a small mind like the others,' and in disgust she withdrew from his presence.

Then Fox came in an effort to win the maiden as his wife. And for a whole day he cut capers and chased his tail round and round in a circle, trying to amuse the serious girl. But he did not succeed very well, and like Loon he departed in despair. And many others came, but they met the same fate, and at last the girl decided to see no more of them, but to live alone with her father.

The young men of the village were all very angry because the girl had spoken of them all so scornfully, and often they talked among themselves of her proud and haughty air. 'She calls us "Scattered-brains",' said one. 'She says we have small minds,' said another. 'She must pay for these insults,' said a third. So they vowed that they would somehow break her proud spirit and bring her sorrow because of her ideas and her decision to stay single all her life. One of the great men of the village was Whirlwind. He could make himself invisible and he was often guilty of many wicked pranks. So the young men went to him and asked his aid in humbling the pride of the haughty maiden. As they were talking to him, they saw the girl approaching not far off. And quite unawares, Whirlwind rushed towards her and knocked her down in the mud and tore her hat from her head and swept it into the sea. The young men looked on at her plight and they all laughed loudly, and the girl was very much ashamed. She went back home and told her father what had happened and showed him her soiled clothes and her blown hair falling about her face. Her father was very angry, and he said: 'Whirlwind must pay for this. He shall be banished at once.'

Then her father went to the Chief and made complaint against Whirlwind, and the Chief decreed that Whirlwind must leave the village forthwith. He did not consider very carefully what the result of this decree might be, and he acted hastily and without thought, for he feared to differ from the wise man. So Whirlwind prepared to leave the place.

Now his best friend was Rain. Rain had been born without eyes. He was black-blind, and Whirlwind always had to lead him along wherever he wished to go. So Rain said: 'If you are leaving the village, I want to leave it too, for I cannot live here without you. I will be helpless if I have no one to lead me.' So the two set out together, Whirlwind leading old Rain along by his side. Where they went no man knew, for they had told nobody of their destination. They were gone for many months be-

fore the people missed them very much. Then their absence began to be felt in all the land, for there was no
wind and there was no rain.

At last the Chief summoned a council, and the decree
of banishment against Whirlwind was revoked. The
people decided to send messengers to the two wandering
ones to tell them what had happened and to bring them
back. So they first sent Fox out on the quest. Fox went
through the land for many weeks, running as fast as he
could over many roads, in and out among marshy lake
shores and over high wooded mountains. He searched
every cave and crevice, but he had no success. Not a leaf
or a blade of grass was stirring, and the country was all
parched and the grass was withered brown and the
streams were all getting dry. At last, after a fruitless
search, he came home and shamefully confessed that his
quest had failed.

Then the people called on Bear to continue the search.
And Bear went lumbering over the earth, sniffing the air,
and turning over logs and great rocks with his powerful
shoulders, and venturing into deep caverns. And he
made many inquiries, and he asked the Mountain Ash:
'Where is Whirlwind?' But Mountain Ash said: 'I do not
know. I have not seen him for many months.' And he
asked the Red Fir, and the Pine, and the Aspen (which
always sees Whirlwind first), but they were all ignorant
of his whereabouts. So Bear came home and said: 'Not
a trace of either of them have I found.'

The Chief was very angry because of the failure of Fox
and Bear, but the wise man said: 'The animals are useless in a quest like this. Let us try the birds. They often
succeed where the animals fail.' And the Chief agreed,

for the land was in great distress. Many fishing-boats lay silent on the sea near the coast, unable to move because Whirlwind was away, and the wells and streams were all dry because Rain was absent, and the grass and the flowers were withering to decay. So they called the birds to their aid.

The great Crane searched in the shallows and among the reeds, thrusting his long neck into deep places, and Crow looked among the hills, and Kingfisher flew far out to sea, but they all came back and said: 'We, too, have failed. The wandering ones are nowhere on the land or upon the sea.'

Then little Sparrow took up the search. Before he set out, he plucked from his breast a small down-feather and fastened it to a stick no bigger than a wisp of hay. He held the stick in his bill and flew off. For many days he went towards the Southland, all the time watching the feather hanging to the stick in his bill. But it hung there motionless. One day, after he had travelled a great distance, he saw the down-feather moving very gently, and he knew that Whirlwind must be not far away. He went in the direction from which the feather was blowing. Soon he saw beneath him soft green grass and wonderful flowers of varied colours, and trees with green leaves and many rippling streams of running water. And he said to himself: 'At last I have found the wanderers.' He followed a little stream for some distance until it ended in a cave in the hills. In front of the cave many flowers were blooming and the grass was soft and green, and the tall grasses were nodding their heads very gently. He knew that those he was seeking were inside, and he entered the cave very quietly. Just beyond the door a

fire was smouldering, and near it lay Rain and Whirlwind, both fast asleep. Sparrow tried to wake them with
his bill and his cries, but they were sleeping too soundly.
Then he took a coal from the fire and put it on Rain's
back, but it spluttered and fizzled and soon went out. He
tried another, but the same thing happened. Then he
took a third coal, and this time Rain woke up. He was
much surprised to hear a stranger in the cave, but he
could not see him because he was blind. So he woke up
Whirlwind to protect him.

Then Sparrow told them of the great trouble in the
north country and of the great hardships and sorrow
their absence had brought to the people, and of how
sadly they had been missed and of the decision of the
council to call them back. And Whirlwind said: 'We
shall return tomorrow if we are so badly needed. You
may go back and tell your people that we are coming.
We shall be there the day after you arrive.' So Sparrow,
feeling very proud of his success, flew back home. But
when he arrived after many days he went first to his own
people to tell them the good news. And the Sparrow-
people all gathered together and held a feast of cele-
bration, and they twittered and danced and made a great
hubbub in their excitement because Rain was coming
back on the morrow. Then Sparrow went to the Chief
and said: 'Oh, Chief, I have found Rain and Whirlwind,
and tomorrow they will be here,' and he told the story of
his flight to the south and of his discovery. And the Chief
said: 'Because of your success, you will never be hunted
for game or killed for food.'

The next morning the two travellers who had been so
long away came back to the land. Whirlwind came first,

and great clouds of dust foretold his coming, and the sea dashed high against the rocks, and the trees shrieked and tossed their heads, all dancing gaily because of his return. When Whirlwind had passed by, Rain came along, following close because of his blindness. For several days Rain stayed with the people, and the flowers bloomed, and the grass was green again, and the wells and streams were no longer dry. And since that time Wind and Rain have never long been absent from the Atlantic coast. And to this day the Sparrow-people know when Rain is coming, and to signal his approach they gather together and twitter and hop along and make a great hubbub, just as they did when their ancestor found him by means of his down-feather in the olden days. But the Indians have been true to the Chief's promise, and they will not hunt sparrows for food or for their feathers. For they remember that of all the birds it was old Sparrow who long ago searched successfully for the Rain.

Rainbow and the Autumn Leaves

In olden days, long before the Indians came to Canada, all the animals talked and worked like men. Every year after midsummer they held a great council at which they were all present. But it happened once in the summer before the council met that they all wanted to go to the sky to see what the country up there was like. None of them could find a way to go.

The oldest and wisest creature on all the earth was Turtle. One day he prayed to the Thunder God to take him to the sky, and his prayer was soon answered. There was a great noise, as if the earth had been split asunder, and when the people next looked for Turtle he was nowhere to be found. They searched everywhere without success. But that evening, when they looked upwards, they saw him in the sky, moving about like a black cloud.

Turtle liked the sky so well that he decided to live there always and to send his descendants, later, to the earth. And the sky-people agreed to keep him. They asked him: 'Where do you want to dwell?' And he answered: 'I should like to dwell in the Black Cloud in which are the ponds and streams and lakes and springs of water, for I always dwelt near these places when I was young.' So he was allowed to have his wish. But when the Great Council of the animals met on earth in the time of the harvest-moon, he was always present. He came in the Black Cloud, but he always went back to the sky after the Council was ended. And the other animals envied him his good fortune, and they wished that they could go with him.

After a time the animals were greatly distressed and angered by the rumour that a new race of creatures was coming from far over the ocean to inhabit their land. They talked it over very carefully, and they all thought how fortunate it would be if they could all go to the sky with old Turtle, and live like him, free from fear and trouble and care. But they were puzzled to know how to get there, for Turtle had never told any of them the way.

One day Deer, wandering about alone in the forest, as was his custom, came across Rainbow, who often built a path of many colours to the sky. And he said to Rainbow: 'Carry me up to the sky, for I want to see Turtle.' But Rainbow was afraid to do it, for he wished first to ask the Thunder God for permission, and he put Deer off, and to gain time he said: 'Come to me in winter when I stay for a time on the mountain near the lake. Then I will gladly carry you to the place where Turtle dwells.'

Throughout the long winter months Deer looked longingly for Rainbow, but Rainbow did not come. Life was growing harder on the earth, and the animals were in terror of the new race that was soon to come to their land,

and Deer was very timid and impatient. At last, one day in the early summer, Rainbow came again, and Deer hastened to meet him. 'Why were you false to me?' he asked. 'I waited for you all winter long on the mountain by the lake, but you did not come as you promised. I want to go to the sky now, for I must see Turtle.' Rainbow answered: 'I cannot take you now. But some day, when there is a fog over the lake, I shall come back to drive it away. Come to me then, and I shall take you to the sky and to the place where Turtle dwells. This time I will not deceive you.'

Rainbow consulted the Thunder God, and received permission to do as Deer wished. Soon afterwards the fog one day rolled in a thick bank across the lake, and Deer hurried to wait for Rainbow. Sure enough, Rainbow came down, as he had promised, to drive the fog away. He threw his arch of many colours from the lake to the blue hills far away, and the fog at once disappeared from the place. And he said to Deer, who stood watching him: 'Now I will keep my promise. Follow my many-coloured path over the hills and the forests and the streams, and be not afraid, and you will soon reach Turtle's home in the sky.' Deer did as he was told, and soon he reached the sky. Turtle was glad to see him, and Deer liked the country so well that he decided to stay forever. And he roamed over the sky everywhere, moving like the wind from place to place.

When midsummer had passed and the harvest-moon had come and the Great Council again met together, Deer was absent for the first time in his life. The animals waited long for him to appear, for they needed his advice, but he did not come. They sent the birds out to find him.

Black Hawk and Woodpecker and Bluejay all sought him in the forest, but they could not find a trace of him. Then Wolf and Fox scoured the woods far and near, but they came back and reported that he could not be found anywhere. At last Turtle arrived at the meeting of the Great Council, as was his custom, coming in his Black Cloud in which were the ponds and lakes and streams and springs of water. And Bear said: 'Deer is absent from the Council meeting. Where is Deer? We cannot meet without him, for we need his advice.' And Turtle replied: 'Deer is in the sky. Have you not heard? Rainbow made a wonderful pathway for him of many varied colours, and by that he came to the sky. There he is now,' and he pointed to a golden cloud scurrying across the sky overhead.

Turtle advised that the animals should all go to the sky to live until they could be sure that the new race of creatures would bring them no harm. And he showed them the pathway that Rainbow had made, stretching from the earth in wonderful colours. The animals all agreed at the Great Council to take Turtle's advice. But they were all very angry at Deer for leaving them without warning, for they thought that all the animals should either stay together faithfully on the earth or go all together to the sky. Bear showed the greatest anger and annoyance. Because of his great strength, he had no fear of the new race that was said soon to be coming, and he had always been inclined to look with scorn on Deer's timid and impatient ways. 'Deer has forsaken us,' he said; 'he deserted us in the hour of our danger, and that is contrary to forest laws and to our code of defence.' And he thought to himself: 'I shall punish him for this when the time comes.'

In the late autumn, the time agreed upon came for the animals to leave the earth, and Rainbow again made his bright path for them to the sky. Bear was the first to go up because he was the leader and because with his great weight he wanted to test the strength of the bridge of burning colours over which they had to pass. When he had almost reached the sky, he met Deer on the path waiting to welcome the animals to their new home. And he said to him in anger: 'Why did you leave us behind, without warning, for the land of the Turtle? Why did you desert the Great Council? Why did you not wait until all could come together? You are a traitor to your comrades and you have been false to our faith.' And Deer answered, also in anger: 'Who are you to doubt me or my faith? None but the Wolf may ask me why I came or question my fidelity. I will kill you for your insolence.' Deer had grown very proud since he had gone to live in the sky, and he was no longer timid as he had been on earth. His eyes flashed in his fury and he arched his neck and lowered his antlered head and rushed madly at Bear to push him from the path.

But Bear was not afraid, for he had often tested his strength with Deer upon the earth. His low, hoarse growls sounded all over the sky, and he prepared to fight. They came together with a shock. For a long time they battled, until the bridge of burning colours trembled and the heavens shook from the force of the conflict.

The animals waiting by the lake at the end of the path looked up and saw the battle above them. They feared the results, for they wanted neither Bear nor Deer to die.

So they sent Wolf up to the sky to put a stop to the contest. When Wolf reached the combatants, Bear was bleeding freely, for Deer with his antlers had pierced his neck and side. Deer, too, was bleeding where Bear's strong claws had torn a great wound in his head. Wolf soon stopped the battle, and Bear and Deer went away to dress their wounds. Then the other animals went up to the sky over Rainbow's flaming path. And they decided to live in the sky and to send their descendants back to earth when the new race of creatures should come. And they can still sometimes be seen, like clouds hurrying across the sky in the shape they had on earth.

But the blood of Bear and of Deer dropped from them as they moved to the sky from the scene of their battle along the Rainbow road. It fell freely upon the leaves beneath them and changed them into varied colours. And every year when autumn comes in the north country, the leaves take on again the bright and wondrous colours given to them by the blood of Bear and Deer when they fought on the Rainbow path ages and ages ago. And Bear and Deer have never since been friends, and their descendants no longer dwell together in peace, as they did in the olden days.

The Passing of Glooskap

Glooskap, the magic master of the Indian tribes along the Atlantic coast of Canada, had very great power for many ages. But as he grew old, his power gradually grew less. He had done in his long lifetime many great and noble deeds. He had freed his land of all the mighty monsters that had inhabited it before his coming. No evil beasts nor serpents nor dragons were now found near his home, and there were no longer cruel giants in the forest hard by. He had made his people happy. But, strangely enough, his people showed him but scanty gratitude. When he grew old they became evil, and they were not as faithful as in the days of his youth and strength. Even the animals grew treacherous. His dogs, once loyal, were no longer eager to do his bidding, and one stormy day, as he fished for porpoises, they stubbornly refused to obey his command to head off the fish. Thereupon, in anger, he changed his dogs into a stone island, now a rocky light-house island on the Atlantic coast. All around him he saw signs of faithlessness, and often he was in great sorrow because of his people's ingratitude.

One afternoon in the autumn, Glooskap walked alone by the ocean, thinking silently of his people's evil ways and of his own vanished strength. Behind him the tall trees rose on the hills, their leaves now turned to a mass of many colours, yellow and red under the autumn sun. Here and there clusters of red autumn berries peeped through the dying leaves. On the high bank long stalks of golden-rod nodded their faded heads; the grass was withered brown, and from its depths came the doleful sounds of crickets. Before him lay the sea, still and idle and grey in the soft mellow light. Subdued noises came from the tents near by, where his people, busy and expectant, were making arrows for the great annual autumn hunt, for the hunter's moon had come. Otherwise a strange silence—the silence of Nature's death—filled the air. Glooskap knew, as he moodily walked along the beach, that Summer had gone, that she had fled from the Northland, following the moose-hide cord he had placed for her along the Rainbow Road to the Wilderness of Flowers. Closing his eyes, he could see her again in all her beauty as he had really seen her many years before when he had first found her dancing among her children, the Fairies of Flowers and Light. All the incidents of his long journey in search of her came back to him—the sail with Old Blob the Whale; the Southern Cross in the sky; the song of the clams under the golden sands; the lilac country with its magnolia and jessamine; the fair maiden dancers on the green; and Summer herself with her brown hair and her blossoms. Even his lost youth and his vanished strength seemed to come back to him. He could feel on his old cheeks again the soft air of the Southland; he could hear the music of its tiny streams; and he opened his nostrils wide in fancy to pleasant odours from scented flowers. And as he dreamed of the old days, he was lonely for Summer, his Fairy Queen; for, although he was a great warrior, he had a woman's tender heart. Somehow on this autumn day he was filled with a strange feeling of melancholy such as he had never known before. He could not shake the feeling from him. It brought him a deep sense of coming danger which he could not explain.

Suddenly he was aroused from his dreaming by the appearance of his messengers, the Loons, who were still loyal to him. They had been away many days in search of news, and now they came to him over the water uttering strange cries that sounded like foolish laughter. Glooskap knew from their cries that they brought unwelcome tidings. When they met him on the beach they said: 'Oh, Master, we bring you a sad message. From away across the ocean a race of strange pale-faced men is coming, smaller in size than our people but more powerful. One of their number is more than a match for a score of your best warriors, for they carry with them many deadly weapons the like of which you have never seen. They are coming in wonderful ships greater than your canoes. They will take all your lands and will kill those of your people who refuse to submit to their rule.' The Loons would have continued their story, but Glooskap wished to hear no more. He understood now the cause of his melancholy dread. He knew that the pale race of which the Loons had spoken was the race of which he had long heard, and that the white men were coming at last. He knew too that it would be useless to stay to give them battle. His reign on earth, he knew well, was ended for a time, and now he must go away. Far out to sea was an-other hunting ground to which he must sail to join his fathers. It was a place, he had been told, pleasanter by far than his old home on the shores of the great water—a place to which good warriors went when their work on earth was done. So he returned silently to his tent to get ready for his long journey.

That night he called all his people to the gathering-place. He told them that he was going away, far away, miles and miles over the sunlit sea. Not one of them should go with him. He would be away, he said, many long years, but some day he would come back. He told them nothing of the message of the Loons, nothing of the white men's coming. But he offered as a parting gift to grant them each one last wish. And at once all the people wished for what they most desired, and all their requests were granted, for Glooskap's great power returned for a brief space before he went away.

The people's wishes were very strange and varied. An old man who had been of little value as a hunter asked that he might be great in the killing of game. And Gloos-kap gave him a magic flute which when played upon won the love of women and brought the moose and caribou to his side to meet their death. And the old man, with not a care in his heart, went his way, for he knew now that he should always have food. A young Indian asked that he might have the love of many people. Glooskap gave him a bag very tightly tied; he told him not to open it until he reached his home, and then his wish would be granted.

But the youth, being curious, opened the bag on the way. At once there flew from it numberless girls, all of whom strove for his affection until in the struggle they trampled him to death. What became of the people no man knows. Another, a gay and frivolous fellow, asked that he might always amuse people. Glooskap gave him a magic root from the forest which would cause anyone who ate it to amuse all whom he met; he told him not to eat it until he reached his home, and then his presence would always be like sunshine to all. But he, being curious, ate the root on the way. For a time he amused all who met him so that they all laughed and were of a merry heart. But soon, because he had not heeded Glooskap's command, the people grew tired of him and no longer laughed at him. And he grew weary of himself and found no pleasure in his power, which now no longer moved people to laughter. And his life became a burden until in despair he killed himself in the forest. And Old Night Hawk, the evil spirit of the night, came down from the clouds and carried him away to the dwelling-place of Darkness and he was never afterwards heard of among men. Another wished to become a Fairy of the Forest. Glooskap washed him in the sea and put a magic belt around his waist, and at once he became a Fairy Prince dwelling among the Elves. And he gave him a small pipe which made wondrous music, and to this day you can hear his pipe on sunny days in the meadows.

But the wish that was most difficult to gratify, for it tried Glooskap's greatest power, was that of a youth who wanted to win a beautiful girl for his wife. She was the daughter of a powerful Chief who placed such hard work and cruel tasks on all who desired her that they died in attempting them. Glooskap gave him his stone canoe and bade him sail away to the Chief's home; he gave the Fairies of the Deep charge over him, and he tied the wings of the great Eagle, the Wind Bird, so that there might be no wind during his voyage. He gave him also a magic belt and taught him a magic song, both of which should help him in his need.

Soon the youth came without mishap to a large island, the home of the girl he loved. He hid the canoe in the trees and set out inland. At the end of a long road he reached the village where the cruel Chief and his daughter lived. He said to the Chief, after the fashion of Indians when they want to marry: 'I am tired of the lonely life; I have come for your daughter.' The Chief replied that the youth might have his daughter if he could do certain feats of strength. The youth knew that these were the feats the attempt of which had cost many before him their lives, but trusting to Glooskap's help, he consented. The Chief told him he must slay a great horned dragon that lived in the forest hard by, and that he must bring the dragon's head to his tent on the following morning.

In the night the youth went to the dragon's den. Over the mouth of it he placed a great log; then standing near it he sang the magic song that Glooskap had taught him. Soon the dragon came out in answer to the magic call; he waved his head all about looking for the sound; then he placed his head over the log to listen. At once the youth severed the creature's head with a blow of his axe, and taking it by one of its great horns, he brought it in the morning to the Chief's camp. And the Chief, greatly surprised, said to himself: 'I fear he will win my daughter.'

There were other difficult feats to try the young man's

courage, but all of them he did without harm to himself and with great wonder to the old Chief.

Finally the Chief used one of his last and hardest tests. He said: 'There is a man of my tribe who has never been beaten in running. You must race with him and beat him if you would win my daughter; you must both run around the world.' The old man was sure that here at last the youth would fail. But the youth put on the magic belt that Glooskap had given him, and when all the people were gathered to watch the contest, he met his rival without fear. He said to the Chief's runner: 'What do men call you?' And he answered: 'I am Northern Light; and what do men call you?' The youth answered: 'I am Chain-Lightning.'

The starting signal was given by the Chief, and the two rivals set out on their race. In a moment they were out of sight, away behind the distant hills. The people all waited patiently for their return. Soon the youth, Chain-Lightning, appeared; he had been around the world, but he was not breathing hard and he was not even tired from his long run. There was yet no sign of his rival. Late in the evening Northern Light came in; but he was very weary, and as he came near he trembled and tottered. He confessed that he had not been all around the world; he had turned back, for Chain-Lightning had gone too fast for him, yet he was very tired. He admitted his defeat. The people wondered greatly at the power of the victorious youth. And the old Chief said: 'I fear he has won my daughter.'

There was still a final test. The Chief said: 'There is a man of my tribe who has never been overcome in diving and swimming under water. You must strive with him and defeat him if you would win my daughter.' And the youth agreed. Again he put on the magic belt and met his rival without fear. When they met by the sea the youth asked the Chief's swimmer: 'What do men call you?' And he replied: 'I am Black Duck; and what do men call you?' He answered: 'I am Loon.' When the Chief gave the signal, they dived and swam under water. In a few minutes Black Duck rose again, for he was out of breath; but the people waited in wonder many hours before Loon rose; and when he came up he was not tired, but laughed heartily. And the old Chief, well content, said to him: 'My tests are ended; you have won my daughter.' That night the great wedding feast was held; and the youth, taking with him his bride, set sail for his home in Glooskap's canoe.

A few of those who asked gifts Glooskap punished before he went away, because of their foolish requests. One who came was very tall and proud of his good looks. He always covered his moccasins with bright beads, and wore coloured coats, and sprinkled himself with strange perfumes, and on the top of his cap he wore a long feather. He asked Glooskap to make him taller and straighter than any of his fellows. And when Glooskap heard his wish, to punish him for his pride he changed him at once to a pine tree. He made him very tall and straight until his head rose above the forest. There he stands to this day, the high green feather in his cap weaving always in the wind. And when the wind blows you can still hear him singing with a moaning voice: 'I am a great man, I am a beautiful Indian, taller than my fellows.' Many others Glooskap punished, but all who had diseases he healed and sent away happy.

When Glooskap knew that the wishes of all the good people who had obeyed his commands had been granted, he was ready to set out on his journey. One day on the shore of the wide ocean he made a great feast to which all his people came and all the animals with them. But it was not a merry gathering, for they knew that they met with Glooskap for the last time before his long absence. In the late autumn afternoon, when the feast was ended, Glooskap prepared to leave them. He threw his kettle into the sea, for he would need it no more, and it became an island. And he tied one wing of the Wind Bird, so that after he had gone away the gales would not blow so strong on the Atlantic coast as they had blown in his lifetime. And he talked long to his people and smoked his last pipe with them and gave them good advice. He spoke of his going away, but of the land to which he was going he would say nothing. He promised that some day after many years had passed he would come again among them.

Then in the evening a great stone canoe came over the ocean, guided by two of the Children of Light. And Glooskap, seeing it, said: 'It is now the sunset hour and I must leave you.' Many of his people, his good followers who throughout his lifetime had been faithful to him, begged him to allow them to go with him. But he answered: 'No, this last great journey I must make alone, for no man can come with me or help me.' And just at the turn of the tide, as the sun set behind the distant hills, he embarked in the great stone canoe and sailed far out to sea with the ebbing tide, singing as he went a strange, sad song. His people and all the beasts looked after him until, in the deepening twilight, they could see him no

more; but long after they had lost sight of him, his song
came to them, weird and doleful, across the water. Gradually the sounds grew fainter and fainter, until when
night came they died entirely away.

Then a strange silence fell upon the earth. The beasts
mourned until they lost the power of speech; they fled
into the forest in different ways, and since that time they
have never met together in peaceful council as in the
olden days, and they have never spoken like men. The
Great Owl departed in sorrow and hid himself in the
deep forest; since that time he has seldom appeared by
day, but at night he always cries, 'Koo-koo-koo,' which in
the Indian language means: 'I am sad, I am sad.' And the

Loon, Glooskap's old messenger, wanders up and down upon the beach calling for his master with loud wild cries. And Glooskap's people grow smaller and smaller in number because of their master's absence, and they slowly waste away until some day they too shall vanish from the earth.

So Glooskap sailed away over the sea to the distant hunting grounds of his fathers. There he lives still in a great long tent where he is making arrows, preparing for his last Great Battle. And when the thunder rolls and the lightning flashes, those of his people who still remain on earth know that he is angry; where the sea sparkles most brightly in the sunlight or moans most dismally in the storm, they know that Glooskap is there; when the phosphorescent lights appear at night upon the sea, they know that he is working late by the strange light; and when there are no stars, they know that Glooskap lies asleep, taking his rest. But when his great tent is filled with arrows, Glooskap will come back to fight his last battle and overcome the evil creatures of the world. He will then bring back the Golden Age of happiness to earth; and his people in hope and patience still await his coming.

The Indian Cinderella

On the shores of a wide bay on the Atlantic coast there dwelt in old times a great Indian warrior. It was said that he had been one of Glooskap's best helpers and friends and that he had done for him many wonderful deeds. But that, no man knows. He had, however, a very wonderful and strange power: he could make himself invisible; he could thus mingle unseen with his enemies and listen to their plots. He was known among the people as Strong Wind the Invisible. He dwelt with his sister in a tent near the sea, and his sister helped him greatly in his work. Many maidens would have been glad to marry him, and he was much sought-after because of his mighty deeds; and it was known that Strong Wind would marry the first maiden who could see him as he came home at night. Many made the trial, but it was a long time before one succeeded.

Strong Wind used a clever trick to test the truthfulness of all who sought to win him. Each evening, as the day went down, his sister walked on the beach with any girl who wished to make the trial. His sister could always see him, but no one else could see him. And as he came home from work in the twilight, his sister, as she saw him drawing near, would ask the girl who sought him: 'Do you see him?' And each girl would falsely answer: 'Yes.' And his sister would ask: 'With what does he draw his sled?' And each girl would answer: 'With the hide of a moose,' or 'With a pole,' or 'With a great cord.' And then his sister would know that they all had lied, for their answers were mere guesses. And many tried and lied and failed, for Strong Wind would not marry any who were untruthful.

There lived in the village a great Chief who had three daughters. Their mother had long been dead. One of these was much younger than the others. She was very beautiful and gentle and well beloved by all, and for that reason her older sisters were very jealous of her charms and treated her very cruelly. They clothed her in rags that she might be ugly, and they cut off her long black hair, and they burned her face with coals from the fire that she might be scarred and disfigured. And they lied to their father, telling him that she had done these things herself. But the young girl was patient and kept her gentle heart and went gladly about her work.

Like other girls, the Chief's two oldest daughters tried to win Strong Wind. One evening, as the day went down, they walked on the shore with Strong Wind's sister and waited for his coming. Soon he came home from his day's work, drawing his sled. And his sister asked as usual: 'Do you see him?' And each one, lying, answered: 'Yes.' And she asked: 'Of what is his shoulder-strap made?' And each, guessing, said: 'Of rawhide.' Then they entered the tent, where they hoped to see Strong Wind eating his supper, and when he took off his coat and his moccasins they could see them, but more than these they saw nothing. And Strong Wind knew that they had lied, and he kept himself from their sight, and they went home dismayed.

One day the Chief's youngest daughter with her rags and her burnt face resolved to seek Strong Wind. She patched her clothes with bits of birch bark from the trees and put on the few little ornaments she possessed and went forth to try to see the Invisible One as all the other girls of the village had done before. And her sisters laughed at her and called her 'Fool'; and as she passed along the road, all the people laughed at her because of her tattered frock and her burnt face, but silently she went her way.

Strong Wind's sister received the little girl kindly, and at twilight she took her to the beach. Soon Strong Wind came home drawing his sled. And his Sister asked: 'Do you see him?' And the girl answered: 'No'; and his sister wondered greatly because she spoke the truth. And again she asked: 'Do you see him now?' And the girl answered: 'Yes, and he is very wonderful.' And she asked: 'With what does he draw his sled?' And the girl answered: 'With the Rainbow,' and she was much afraid. And she asked further: 'Of what is his bow-string?' And the girl answered: 'His bow-string is the Milky Way.'

Then Strong Wind's sister knew that because the girl had spoken the truth at first, her brother had made himself visible to her. And she said: 'Truly, you have seen him.' And she took her home and bathed her, and all the scars disappeared from her face and body; and her hair grew long and black again like the raven's wing; and she gave her fine clothes to wear and many rich ornaments. Then she bade her take the wife's seat in the tent. Soon Strong Wind entered and sat beside her and called her his bride. The very next day she became his wife, and ever afterwards she helped him to do great deeds. The girl's two elder sisters were very cross and they wondered greatly at what had taken place. But Strong Wind, who knew of their cruelty, resolved to punish them. Using his great power, he changed them both into aspen trees and rooted them in the earth. And since that day the leaves of the aspen have always trembled, and they shiver in fear at the approach of Strong Wind, it matters not how softly he comes, for they are still mindful of his great power and anger because of their lies and their cruelty to their sister long ago.

The Duck with Red Feet

A hunter in old times lived on the bank of a river far away in the Canadian forest. He passed all his days in the deep woods where he had great success in catching and killing game. There was no better hunter than he in all the country. Every evening he returned to his home, bringing his day's catch with him. His father and mother were both dead and he had no sister. He had only one brother. This brother was very small. He was so small that the hunter kept him in a little box; when he went away in the morning to hunt, he always closed the box up tight so that his little brother could not get out, for he feared that if he got out, harm would come to him. Every night he took him out of the box to give him food, and the little man was so hungry that he always ate a great lot of food. The little man slept always with his brother, but every morning he was carefully locked up in the box. And in time he grew tired of his prison.

One evening as the hunter came down the river from

his hunting journey he saw a very beautiful girl sitting on the bank of the stream. He decided he would catch her and take her home to be his wife, for he was lonely. He paddled to the beach as silently as he could, but she saw him coming and she jumped into the water and disappeared. She went to her home at the bottom of the river and told her mother that the hunter had tried to catch her. But her mother told her that she should not have run away. She said: 'The hunter who tried to catch you was intended to be your husband. You must wait for him tomorrow and tell him you will be his wife.'

The next night, as the hunter came down the river, the girl was again sitting on the bank. He paddled over as he had done on the evening before, but this time she did not run away. She said: 'I have been waiting for you. You may take me for your wife.' And the man, well pleased with his beautiful prize, placed her in his canoe and took her home.

He did not tell her of his little brother in the box. He cooked a beaver for the evening meal. He and his wife ate half of it, but he placed the other half away in the cupboard. Then he told his wife to go to sleep, and she went to bed and soon fell asleep. When she awoke in the morning her husband had gone for his day's hunting, for he had to leave early to go a long distance into the forest. She found too that the half of the beaver he had put in the cupboard was gone. And she wondered what had become of it.

That evening, when her husband came home, he cooked another beaver for their meal. Again they ate half of it, and the man placed the other half of it to one side. But not a word did he say of his brother in the box. Then the man sent his wife to bed as on the previous night, and soon she was fast asleep. When she awoke in the morning, her husband was gone for his day's hunting. The half of the beaver which he had placed to one side was also gone, but she knew he had not taken it. She was afraid, and all day she wondered where the meat had gone. She decided that she would find out what had happened to it.

That night, when her husband came home, he cooked half a moose for their evening meal. They ate part of it, and the man placed the remainder of it to one side as usual. Then he told his wife to go to sleep. She went to bed and pretended to sleep, but she stayed wide awake, peeping through half-closed eyelids. When her husband thought she was sleeping soundly, he unlocked a little box that stood on a low shelf and took out a little man and gave him the moose meat he had put aside. The little man ate every bit of it. He looked very strange. He was all red from head to heels, as if he were covered with red paint, and he said not a word. When he had greedily eaten all the meat, the man washed him and combed his hair and then put him back in the box and locked him up. The woman wondered greatly at this strange happening, but she could not keep from laughing heartily to herself because of the funny appearance of the little man.

The next day the man left early for his day's hunting. When she was sure he was far away, she thought she would take a peep at the queer little red man in the box. She found the key hanging on the wall, and opened the box and called to the little man to come out. But he would not come. He seemed to be very much afraid of her. She coaxed him to come out, but he refused. Then

she caught him and pulled him out. He looked at her for a long time, but he would say not a word. Then he ran to the door, which was open, and with a sudden jump he sprang into the air and disappeared. The woman called to him but he would not come back. He was never seen again.

The woman was very much afraid. But she was more frightened when she looked at her hands. They were all red because she had caught the little red man, and many red spots were on her arms and on her feet where the red colouring from the man had dropped. She tried to wash off the red spots, but she could not remove them. She washed and rubbed her hands all day, but the stains would not come off.

When her husband came home in the evening, he knew when he saw her red hands what had happened. He knew that his brother of the box had gone, and he was very angry. He seized a rod and ran at her to beat her. She was afraid he would kill her, and she ran to the river and jumped in to go back to her old home. But as she reached the water, she was changed from what she was. At once she became a Sheldrake Duck. The red spots remained on her, and the sea could not wash them off. And to this day the Sheldrake Duck has red stains on her feet and feathers, because she was curious, and took the funny little red man from the box in the olden days.

The Boy Who Was Called 'Thick-head'

Three brothers lived with their old Indian mother in the forest near the sea. Their father had long been dead. At his death he had little of the world's goods to his credit and his widow and her sons were very poor. In the place where they dwelt, game was not plentiful, and to get food enough to keep them from want they had often to go far into the forest. The youngest boy was smaller and weaker than the others, and when the two older sons went far away to hunt, they always left him behind, for although he always wished to accompany them, they would never allow him to go. He had to do all the work about the house, and all day long he gathered wood in the forest and carried water from the stream. And even when his brothers went out in the springtime to draw sap from the maple trees, he was never permitted to go with them. He was always making mistakes and doing foolish things. His brothers called him 'Thick-head', and all the people round about said he was a simpleton because of his slow and queer ways. His mother alone was kind to him, and she always said: 'They may laugh at you and call you "Fool", but you will prove to be wiser than all of them yet, for so it was told me by a forest fairy at your birth.'

The Chief of the people had a beautiful daughter who had many suitors. But her father spurned them all from his door and said: 'My daughter is not yet of age to marry; and when her time of marriage comes, she will only marry the man who can make great profit from hunting.' The two older sons of the old woman decided that one of them must win the girl. So they prepared to set out on a great hunting expedition far away in the northern forest, for it was now autumn, and the hunter's moon had come. The youngest boy wanted to go with them, for he had never been away from home and he wished to see the world. And his mother said he might go. His brothers were very angry when they heard his request, and they said: 'Much good Thick-head can do us in the chase. He will only bring us bad luck. He is not a hunter but a scullion and a drudge fit only for the fireside.' But his mother commanded them to grant the boy's wish and they had to obey. So the three brothers set out for the north country, the two older brothers grumbling loudly because they were accompanied by the boy they thought a fool.

The two older brothers had good success in the chase and they killed many animals—deer and rabbits and otters and beavers. And they came home bearing a great quantity of dried meat and skins. They each thought: 'Now we have begun to prove our prowess to the Chief, and if we succeed as well next year when the hunter's moon comes again, one of us will surely win his daughter when she is old enough to marry.' But all the youngest boy brought home as a result of his journey into the game country was a large Earthworm as thick as his finger and as long as his arm. It was the biggest Earthworm he had ever seen. He thought it a great curiosity as well as a great discovery, and he was so busy watching it each day that he had no time to hunt. When he brought it home in a box, his brothers said to their mother: 'What did we tell you about Thick-head? He has now surely proved himself a fool. He has caught only a fat Earthworm in all these weeks.' And they noised it abroad in the village and all the people laughed loudly at the simpleton, until 'Thick-head's hunt' became a byword in all the land. But the boy's mother only smiled and said: 'He will surprise them all yet.'

The boy kept the Earthworm in a tiny pen just out-side the door of his home. One day a large Duck came waddling along and, sticking her bill over the little fence of the pen, she quickly gobbled up the Worm. The boy was very angry, and he went to the man who owned the Duck and said: 'Your Duck ate up my pet Worm. I want my Worm.' The man offered to pay him whatever price he asked, but the boy said: 'I do not want your price. I want my Worm.' But the man said: 'How can I give you your Worm when my Duck has eaten it up? It is gone for-ever.' And the boy said: 'It is not gone. It is in the Duck's belly, so I must have the Duck.' Then to avoid further trouble the man gave Thick-head the Duck, for he thought to himself: 'What is the use of arguing with a fool?'

The boy took the Duck home and kept it in a little pen near his home with a low fence around it. And he tied

a great weight to its foot so that it could not fly away. He
was quite happy again, for he thought: 'Now I have both
my Worm and the Duck.' But one day a Fox came prowling along looking for food. He saw the fat Duck tied by
the foot in the little pen, and he said: 'What good fortune! There is a choice meal for me,' and in a twinkling
he was over the fence. The Duck quacked and made a
great noise, but she was soon silenced. The Fox had just
finished eating up the Duck when the boy, who had
heard the quacking, came running out of the house. The
Fox was smacking his lips after his good meal and he was
too slow in getting away. The boy fell to beating him
with a stout club and soon killed him and threw his body
into the yard behind the house. And he thought: 'That
is not so bad. Now I have my Worm and the Duck and
the Fox.'

That night an old Wolf came through the forest in
search of food. He was very hungry, and in the bright
moonlight he saw the dead Fox lying in the yard. He
pounced upon it greedily and devoured it until not a
trace of it was left. But the boy saw him before he could
get away, and he came stealthily upon him and killed
him with a blow of his axe.

'I am surely in good luck,' he thought, 'for now I have the Worm and the Duck and the Fox and the Wolf.' But the next day, when he told his brothers of his good fortune and his great skill, they laughed at him loudly and said: 'Much good a dead Wolf will do you. Before two days have passed it will be but an evil-smelling thing and we shall have to bury it deep. You are indeed a great fool.' The boy pondered for a long time over what they had said, and he thought: 'Perhaps they are right. The dead Wolf cannot last long. I will save the skin.'

So he skinned the Wolf and dried the skin and made a drum from it, for the drum was one of the few musical instruments of the Indians in those old times, and they beat it loudly at all their dances and festivals. The boy beat the drum each evening, and made a great noise, and he was very proud because he had the only drum in the whole village. One day the Chief sent for him and said to him: 'I want to borrow your drum for this evening. I am having a great gathering to announce to all the land that my daughter is now of age to marry and that suitors may now seek her hand in marriage. But we have no musical instruments and I want your drum, and I myself will beat it at the dance.' So Thick-head brought his drum to the Chief's house. But he was not very well pleased because he was not invited to the feast, while his brothers were among the favoured guests. And he said to the Chief: 'Be very careful. Do not tear the skin of my drum, for I can never get another like it. My Worm and my Duck and my Fox and my Wolf have all helped to make it.'

The next day he went for his drum. But the Chief had struck it too hard and had split it open so that it would now make no sound, and it was ruined beyond repair. He offered to pay the boy a great price for it, but the boy said: 'I do not want your price. I want my drum. Give me back my drum, for my Worm and the Duck and the Fox and the Wolf are all in it.' The Chief said: 'How can I give you back your drum when it is broken? It is gone forever. I will give you anything you desire in exchange for it. Since you do not like the price I offer, you may name your own price and you shall have it.' And the boy thought to himself: 'Here is a chance for good fortune. Now I shall surprise my brothers.' And he said: 'Since you cannot give me my drum, I will take your daughter in marriage in exchange.' The Chief was much perplexed, but he had to be true to his word. So he gave his daughter to Thick-head, and they were married, and the girl brought him much treasure and they lived very happily. And his brothers were much amazed and angered because they had failed. But his mother said: 'I told you he was wiser than you and that he would outwit you yet, although you called him "Thick-head" and "Fool". For the forest fairy said it to me at his birth.'

The Boy Who Was Saved
by Thoughts

A poor widow woman once lived near the sea in Eastern
Canada. Her husband had been drowned catching fish
one stormy day far off the coast, and her little boy was
now her only means of support. He had no brothers or
sisters, and he and his mother, because they lived alone,
were always good comrades. Although he was very young
and small, he was very strong, and he could catch fish
and game like a man. Every day he brought home food
to his mother, and they were never in want.

Now it happened that the Great Eagle who made the
winds in these parts became very angry because he was
not given enough to eat. He went screaming through the
land in search of food, but no food could he find. And
he said: 'If the people will not give me food, I will take
care that they get no food for themselves, and when I
grow very hungry I shall eat up all the little children in
the land. For my young ones must have nourishment too.'
So he tossed the waters about with the wind of his great

wings, and he bent the trees and flattened the corn, and for days he made such a hurly-burly on the earth that the people stayed indoors and they were afraid to come out in search of food.

At last the boy and his mother became very hungry. And the boy said: 'I must go and find food, for there is not a crumb left in the house. We cannot wait longer.' And he said to his mother: 'I know where a fat young beaver lives in his house of reeds on the bank of the stream near the sea. I shall go and kill him, and his flesh will feed us for many days.' His mother did not want him to make this hazardous journey, for the Great Eagle was still in the land. But he said to her: 'You must think of me always when I am gone, and I will think of you, and while we keep each other in our memories I shall come to no harm.' So, taking his long hunting knife, he set out for the beaver's home in his house of reeds on the bank of the stream near the sea. He reached the place without mishap and there he found Beaver fast asleep. He soon killed him and slung him over his shoulder and started back to his mother's house. 'A good fat load I have here,' he said to himself, 'and we shall now have many a good dinner of roast beaver-meat.'

But as he went along with his load on his back the Great Eagle spied him from a distance and swooped down upon him without warning. Before he could strike with his knife, the Eagle caught him by the shoulders and soared away, holding him in a mighty grip with the beaver still on his back. The boy tried to plunge his knife into the Eagle's breast, but the feathers were too thick and tough and he was not strong enough to drive the knife through them. He could do nothing but make the best of his sorry plight. 'Surely I can think of a way of escape,' he said to himself, 'and my mother's thoughts will be with me to help me.' Soon the Eagle arrived at his home. It was built on a high cliff overlooking the sea, hundreds of feet above the beach, where even the sound of the surf rolling in from afar could not reach it. There were many young birds in the nest, all clamouring for food. Great Eagle threw the boy to the side of the nest and told him to stay there. And he said: 'I shall first eat the beaver, and after he is all eaten up we shall have a good fat meal from you.' Then he picked the beaver to pieces and fed part of it to his young ones.

For some days the boy lay in terror in the nest, trying to think of a way of escape. Birds flew high over his head, and far out on the ocean he could see great ships going by. But no help came to him, and he thought that death would soon be upon him. And his mother sat at home waiting for him to return, but day after day passed and still he did not come. She thought he must surely be in great danger, or that perhaps he was already dead. One day, as she was weeping, thinking of her lost boy, an old woman came along. 'Why do you cry?' she asked. And the weeping woman said: 'My boy has been away for many days. I know that harm has come upon him. The men of my tribe have gone in search of him and they will kill whatever holds him a prisoner, but I fear he will never come back alive.' And the old woman said: 'Little good the men of your tribe can do you! You must aid him with your thoughts, for material things are vain. I will help you, for I have been given great power by the Little People of the Hills.' So the woman used her thoughts and her wishes to bring back her boy.

That night the boy noticed that the beaver had all been eaten up and that not a morsel remained. He knew that unless he could save himself at once he would surely die on the morrow. The Great Eagle, he knew, would swoop down upon him and kill him with a blow of his powerful beak and claws. But when the boy slept, he saw his mother in his slumber. And she said to him: 'To-morrow, when Great Eagle goes from the nest, brace your knife, point upwards, against the rock. When he swoops down to kill you, his breast will strike the knife and he will be pierced to death. You are not strong enough to cut through his feathers with your knife, but he is power-ful enough to destroy himself.' The next morning, when Great Eagle went out, the boy did as the vision of the night had told him. He braced his sharp hunting-knife, point upwards, against the rock and sat still and waited. Then he heard the young eagles making a great noise and crying loudly for their breakfast. He knew that his hour had come.

Soon the Great Eagle, hearing the screams of his young ones, came flying back to the nest to kill the boy. He circled around above him with loud cries, and then with great force swooped down upon him, hoping to kill him with his beak and claws. But instead, he struck the blade braced upwards against the rock. The knife pierced far into his breast, and with a loud scream he rolled over dead into the nest. The boy then killed the young eagles, and he knew that now for a time he was safe.

But he did not know how to get down from the Eagle's nest, for it jutted out like a shelf far over the beach, and behind it was a wall of rock around which he could not

climb. He had no means of making a ladder, and his cries would not be heard upon the beach because of the constant roaring of the surf. He thought he would surely starve to death, and that night he cried himself to sleep. But in the night he again saw his mother in his slumbers. And she said: 'You are a foolish boy. Why do you not use the thoughts I send you? Tomorrow, skin the Eagle and crawl inside the skin. If the wide wings can hold the Eagle in the air they can likewise hold you. Drop off from the cliff and you will land safely on the beach.'

The next day the boy did as the vision of the night had told him. He carefully skinned the Great Eagle. Then he crawled inside the skin and thrust his arms through the skin just above the wings, so that his extended arms would hold the wings straight out beneath them. Then he prepared to drop down. But when he looked over the cliff, he was very frightened, for the sight made him dizzy. On the beach, men looked like flies, they were so far away. But he remembered the promise made to him in his slumbers. So he pushed himself from the cliff and dropped down. The wings of Great Eagle let him fall gently through the air and he landed safely and unhurt upon the beach. He crawled out of the skin and set out for his home. It was a long journey, for Great Eagle had carried him far away, but towards evening he reached his home safely, and his mother received him with great gladness.

The boy began to boast of his adventure, and he told how he had killed Great Eagle and how he had dropped down unscathed from the cliff. He spoke of himself with great pride, and of his strength and his shrewdness. But the old woman from the Land of the Little People (the fairies of the hills), who was still present with his mother, said: 'Oh, vain boy, do not think so highly of yourself. Your strength is nothing; your shrewdness is nothing. It was not these things that saved you, but it was the strength of our thoughts. These alone endure and succeed when all else fails. I have taught you the uselessness of all material things, which in the end are but as ashes or as dust. Our thoughts alone can help us in the end, for they alone are eternal.' And the boy listened and wondered at what the old woman from the Land of Little People had said, but he boasted of his strength no more.

Great Heart and the Three Tests

Somewhere near the sea in olden times a boy was living with his father and mother. He had no brothers or sisters. His father was a great hunter and the boy inherited something of his power, for he was always very successful in the killing of game. And his mother said: 'Some day he will be a great man, for before his birth a vision came to me in the night and told me that my son would win wide fame. And fairy gifts were laid by the fairies in his cradle.' And his father, listening to her boasting, said: 'Time will tell, time will tell; but if he is to be a great man it is his own deeds and not your boasting that must prove it.' As the boy grew up he became strangely beautiful and he had great strength. And his father said: 'It is time he set out to seek his fortune. I was in the forest doing for myself when I was no older than he.' And his mother said: 'Wait a little and be not so impatient. He is yet young and there is yet much time.' So the boy remained at home a while longer.

Now it happened that far away in a distant village there lived a young girl of very great beauty and grace. Her father had been a great Chief, but he was now dead. Her mother too was dead and she was all alone in the world. But her parents had left her vast lands and a great store of goods and many servants, and because of her treasures and her great beauty she had many suitors. But she was not easily pleased by men, and on all who came to seek her hand she imposed severe feats of skill to test their sincerity and their worth. She was carefully guarded by an old woman and many servants who kept troublesome and meddlesome people away.

Soon the fame of the girl's wealth and beauty spread through all the land. It reached the sea-coast village where the young man dwelt. His father thought to himself: 'Here is a good chance for my son to prove his worth.' So he called his boy to him and said: 'It is time you were setting out to seek your fortune in the world and to find a wife, for your springtime is passing and your summer of life will soon be here, and before you know it your autumn will be upon you and your winter will be near. There is no time to lose. Seek out the beautiful girl of the rich treasures in the distant inland village and try to win her as your wife.' And his mother gave him the fairy gifts which had been laid in his cradle at his birth, and he said goodbye to his parents and set out on his long journey. He had no misgivings, for he was very vain of his beauty and he was sure, too, of his strength.

As he travelled inland he came one day upon a man clad in scarlet, sitting on the side of a rocky hill tying stones to his feet. 'Hello!' he said to the man. 'Why are you tying these heavy rocks to your ankles?' 'I am a hunter,' replied the man, 'but when I follow the deer I run so fast that I am soon far in front of them instead of behind them, and I am putting heavy weights on my feet so that I will not run so rapidly.' 'You are indeed a wonderful man,' said the boy; 'but I am alone and I need a companion. Let us go along together.' 'Who are you?' said the man. 'I am Lad of the Great Heart,' said the boy, 'and I can do great deeds and I can win for you great treasure.' So the Scarlet Runner went along with him.

Towards evening when they were now far inland they came to a large lake. Among the trees on the fringe of the lake a large fat man was lying flat on his stomach with his mouth in the water drinking as hard as he could. For some time they watched him, but still he drank and the lake grew smaller and smaller and still his thirst was not quenched. They laughed at such a strange sight, and as they approached him the boy said: 'Hello! Why do you lie there drinking so much water?' 'Oh,' answered the fat man, 'there are times when I cannot get enough water to drink. When I have drunk this lake dry I shall be thirsty.' 'Who are you?' asked the boy. 'I am Man of the Great Thirst,' said the fat man. 'That is well,' said Great Heart. 'We two need a third companion. We can do great deeds and we can win for you great treasure.' So the three went along together.

They had not gone far when they came to a wide open plain where they saw a man walking along with his face raised upwards, peering at the sky. He moved along rapidly and seemed to find his way without his eyes, for he gazed steadily at the heavens. 'Hello!' said Great Heart as the sky-gazer rushed past him and almost knocked him over. 'What are you looking at so intently?' 'Oh,' said the man, 'I have shot an arrow into the sky and I am waiting for it to fall. It has gone so far that it will be some time before it drops.' 'Who are you?' asked the boy. 'I am the Far-Darter,' said the sky-gazer. 'We three need a fourth companion,' said the boy. 'We can do great deeds and win for you much treasure. Come along with us.' So the four went along together.

They had gone but a short distance across the plain to the edge of a forest when they came upon a man lying down at full length with his head upon his hand. The edge of his hand was on the ground and it was half closed around his ear, which rested upon it. As he saw the four men approaching him he placed a finger of his other hand upon his lips and signalled to them to keep quiet. 'Hello!' said Great Heart in a whisper. 'What are you doing there with your ear to the ground?' 'I am listening to the plants growing far away in the forest,' he answered. 'There is a beautiful flower I wish to find, and I am trying to hear it breathing so that I may go and get it. Aha! I hear it now.' So saying, he rose from the ground. The boy said: 'Who are you?' 'I am Keen Ears,' said the listener. 'We four need another companion,' said Great Heart. 'We can do great deeds and win for you much treasure. Come along with us.' So the four men and the boy went along together—Keen Ears, and Scarlet Runner, and Far Darter, and Man of the Great Thirst, and Lad of the Great Heart. Then Great Heart unfolded to the others his plan to win the beautiful girl who lived with her treasures in the distant village. And they gladly agreed to help him in his dangerous undertaking.

When they reached the village the people were all very curious when they saw the five strangers. They marvelled at Great Heart's beauty. But when they heard that he wished to marry the daughter of the former Chief, they shook their heads gravely and said: 'It will never be. She places hard conditions on all who seek her hand. He who fails in the tests is doomed to death. Many suitors have tried and failed and died.' But Great Heart was not a-larmed, and with his four companions he went to the girl's home. The old woman who guarded her met him at the door and he made known his wishes. She laughed scornfully when she saw his great beauty, and she said: 'You look more like a girl than like a warrior. You cannot endure the tests.' But the young man insisted on making the trials.

The old woman said: 'If you fail in the tests you will die,' and Great Heart said: 'It is so agreed.' Then the woman said: 'If you wish to win the maiden you must first push away this great rock from before her window.

It keeps the sunlight from her in the mornings.' Then Great Heart, calling to his aid the fairy gifts of his cradle, placed his shoulder against the huge stone which rose higher than the house and he pushed with all his strength. With a mighty crash it rolled down the hill and broke into millions of pieces. The bits of rock flew all over the earth, so great was the fall, and the little pebbles and stones that came from it are seen throughout the world to this day. The sunlight streamed in at the window, and the maiden knew that the first test had been successfully passed by a suitor.

Then came the second test. The old woman and her servants brought great quantities of food and drink and bade the strangers consume it all at one meal. They were very hungry, for they had eaten nothing all day and they easily ate up the food. But when Great Heart saw the great barrels of water, his spirits sank and he said: 'I fear I am beaten.' But Man of the Great Thirst said: 'Not so fast, my friend. The spell of great stomach-burning is again upon me. I am very dry, as if there was a fire in my belly. Give me a chance to drink.' He went from barrel to barrel and in a twinkling he had drained them all of every drop. And the people wondered greatly.

But there was still another test. 'You must have one of your party run a race,' said the old woman to Great Heart. And she brought out a man who had never been beaten in running. 'Who is your choice of runners?' she asked. 'He must race with this man, and if he wins you may have the maiden for your wife and all the treasure with her, for this is the final test. But if he loses the race you shall die.' Great Heart called Scarlet Runner to the mark and told the old woman that this was the man selected. Then he untied the rocks from the runner's feet, and when all was ready the race began. The course lay far across the plains for many miles until the runners should pass from sight, and back again to the starting point.

The two runners kept together for some distance, talking together in a friendly way as they ran. When they had passed from sight of the village the maiden's runner said: 'Now we are out of sight of the village. Let us rest here a while on this grassy bank, for the day is hot.' The Scarlet Runner agreed to this and they both stretched out on the grass. Now this was an old trick of the maiden's runner, who always won by craft rather than by speed. They had not lain down long on the grass when Scarlet Runner fell asleep under the hot sun, just as his rival had hoped. When the latter was sure that his rival was sound asleep, he set out for the village, running as fast as he could. The people soon saw their runner approaching far off on the plains, but there was no sign of the stranger, and they thought that the new suitor for the girl's hand had at last failed like all the others before him.

Great Heart was much puzzled when Scarlet Runner did not appear, and as he saw the maiden's runner coming nearer, he said: 'What can have happened? I fear I am beaten.' But Keen Ears threw himself flat on the ground and listened. 'Scarlet Runner is asleep,' he called. 'I hear him snoring on the plains far away.' And with his keen sense of sound he located the exact spot where the runner was lying. 'I will soon wake him,' said Far-Darter, as he fitted an arrow to his bow-string. The people all thought him mad, for they had never seen an arrow shot so great a distance beyond their sight. But Far-Darter was not dismayed. He quickly shot an arrow from his bow to the spot which Keen Ears had indicated. His aim was so true that the arrow hit Scarlet Runner on the nose and aroused him from his sleep. But when he rose to his feet he found that his rival was gone and he knew that he had been deceived. So in a great rage because of the trick and the pain in his nose, he set out for the village running like the wind. His rival had almost reached the end of the race, but by putting all his strength into his effort, Scarlet Runner quickly overtook him and passed him near the winning-post and won the race. And the people wondered greatly at these deeds of the strangers.

Then the old woman said to Great Heart: 'You have won the maiden as your wife, for you alone have succeeded in these tests.' So the two were married with great ceremony. Great Heart gave much treasure to his companions, and they promised to help him always in his need. Then with his wife and her servants and her great store of goods he went back to his native village by the sea. His father and mother were glad to see him again and to hear of his success, and his mother said: 'I told you he would win great fame because of the fairy gifts that were laid in his cradle at his birth.' And they all lived together and were henceforth very happy.

Ermine and the Hunter

Far away in the Canadian north country an old man lived with his wife and children. They lived far from other people, but they were never lonely, for they had much work to do. The old man was a great hunter, and in summer he and his wife and children lived on the fish and game he captured in the winter. In the springtime he gathered sap from the maple trees from which he made maple syrup and maple sugar with which to sweeten their food. One day in summer he found three small bears eating his stock of sugar. When he came upon them his sugar was all gone and he was very cross. With a stout club he killed the little bears and skinned them and dried their meat. But his wife said: 'No good can come of it. You should not have killed the three little bears, for they were too young for slaughter.'

The next day the old Bear came along, looking for his lost children. When he saw their skins hanging up to dry, he knew that they had been killed by the hunter. He was

very sad and angry, and he called to the hunter: 'You have killed my little motherless cubs, and in return for that wickedness, some night when you are off your guard I will kill your children, and then I will kill you and your wife and I will devour all your food.'

The old man shot at him with his arrows, but the arrows did not harm him, for he was Brown Bear of the Stony Heart, and he could not be killed by man. For many nights and days the old man tried to trap him, but he met with no success. And each day he saw his store of food growing smaller, for Bear of the Stony Heart stole it always in the night. And he thought: 'We shall all surely starve before the winter comes and game is plentiful again.'

One day in despair he resolved to look about him for someone who would tell him how to kill the bear. He went to the bank of the river and sat there in thought and smoked long at his pipe. And he called to the God of the River and said: 'Oh, River-god! Help me to drown

Bear when he comes to fish.' The river came from the limestone country far back among the rocks, and it was flowing rapidly to the sea. And the River-god said: 'My water cannot tarry. There are millions of oysters down on the ocean shore waiting for shells, and I am hurrying down there with the lime to make them,' and he rushed quickly past.

Then the old man called to the Spirit of the Wind, and he said: 'Oh, Spirit of the Wind! Stay here with me tonight and help me to kill Bear of the Stony Heart. You can knock down great trees upon his back and crush him to the earth.' But the Wind Spirit said: 'I cannot linger. Many ships with rich cargoes lie silent on the ocean waiting to sail, and I must hurry along with the force to drive them.' And, like the River-god, he hastened on his way.

Then the old man called to Storm Cloud, which was just then passing over his head, and he said: 'Oh, Spirit of the Storm Cloud! Stay here with me tonight and help me to kill Bear of the Stony Heart, for he seeks to destroy my children. You can send lightning and thunder to strike him dead.' But the Storm Cloud said: 'I cannot loiter on the way. Far from here there are millions of blades of corn and grass dying from thirst in the summer heat, for I see the heat waves rising on the earth, and I am hurrying there with rain to save them.' And, like the River-god and the Wind Spirit, he hurried along on his business. The poor old man was in great sorrow, for it seemed that no one would help him to rid the land of Bear of the Stony Heart.

As he sat wondering what he should do, an old woman came along. She said: 'I am very hungry and tired, for I

have come far. Will you give me food and let me rest here
a while?' And he said: 'We have very little food, for Bear
of the Stony Heart steals it from us nightly, but you may
share with us what little we have.' So he went away and
brought back to her a good fat meal.

While she was eating her dinner he told her of his
troubles with Bear, and he said that no one would help
him to get rid of the pest, and that Bear could not be
killed by man. And the old woman said: 'There is a little
animal who can kill Bear of the Stony Heart; he alone
can save you. You have done well to me. Here is a wand
which I will give you. Go to sleep here, soon, on the bank
of the river. Wave this wand before you sleep and say
what I shall teach you, and when you awake call to you
the first animal you see when you open your eyes. He will
be the animal of which I speak, and he will rid you of
the Bear.' She taught him a little rhyme and gave him a
wand which she took from the basket on her arm; then
she hobbled away, and the old man knew that she was the
weird woman of the Fairy Blue Mountain, of whom he
had often heard. He marvelled greatly, but he resolved to
do as she had told him.

After the old woman had gone, the man waved the little wand three times, and cried:

> 'Animal, animal, come from your lair!
> Help me to slaughter the old Brown Bear.
> Make with my magic a little white dart,
> To pierce in the centre old Bear's stony heart.'

He repeated the rhyme three times. Then he felt himself
getting drowsy, and sleep soon came upon him. He slept
but a short time when the heat woke him up, for the hot

sun beat down upon him. He rubbed his eyes and looked about him. Watching him from behind a tree was a little animal with a shaggy brown coat. The old man thought to himself: 'Surely the weird fairy woman of the Blue Mountain has played a trick on me. That scraggy little animal with the dirty coat cannot kill the Bear.' But he resolved to test her word. He repeated his rhyme again, and the little animal came quickly towards him.

'Who are you?' said the man.

'I am Ermine,' said the little animal.

'Are you the animal of which the fairy woman of the Blue Hills has told me?' asked the man.

'I am indeed the same,' said Ermine. 'I have been sent to you to kill the Bear, and here I have the little darts made powerful because of your magic wand.' He pointed to his mouth and showed the old man his sharp white teeth.

'So now to your task,' said the old man in high spirits.

'Oh, not so fast,' said Ermine. 'You must first pay me for my work.'

'What can I do for you?' asked the man.

'I am ashamed of my dirty brown coat, which I have worn for a long time,' said the animal. 'You have great magic from the wand you received from the fairy woman of the Blue Hills. I want a sleek and shining white coat that I can wear always, for I want to be clean.'

The man waved his wand again and wished for what the animal had asked him, and at once the shaggy brown coat of Ermine was replaced by a sleek and shining white coat as spotless as the new snow in winter. Then the animal said: 'I have one more condition to impose on you. You must promise never to kill a bear's young cubs

when they are still following their mother in the summer-
time. You must give them a chance to grow strong, so
that they may be able to fight for their own lives.' And the
man promised, placing his hand upon the wand to bind
his oath. Then, when he looked again, the wand had
vanished from his hand. It had gone back through the
air to the fairy woman of the Blue Hills.

Then Ermine set out on his search for Bear. The afternoon was very hot, and the forest was still, and not a leaf
or a blade of grass was stirring, and there was not a ripple
on the stream. The whole world was drowsy in the dry
summer heat. But Ermine did not feel the heat, he was
in such high spirits because of his new white coat.

Soon he came upon Bear, stretched out at full length
on the bank of the river, taking his afternoon nap, as was

his custom after his fat mid-day meal. He was lying on his back, and his mouth was open wide, and he was snoring loudly like a waterfall. 'This is your last sleep,' said Ermine, creeping softly to his side, 'for you are a dangerous thief; you shall snore no more.' And with a bound he jumped down Bear's throat and in an instant had pierced with his teeth his strong stony heart, which the arrows of the Indians could never reach. Then as quickly as he had entered the Bear's mouth, Ermine jumped out again and ran from the place. Bear snored no more; he was quite dead, and the land was rid of his thefts and terrors.

Then Ermine went back to the old man and told him that the deed was done; and that night was a great feast night in the old man's home. And since that time Ermine in the north country has worn a sleek white coat as spotless as the new snow in winter. And to this day the hunters in the far north will not kill, if they can avoid it, the young bear cubs while they are still following their mothers through the forest. They give them a chance to grow up and grow strong so that they may be able to fight for their own lives, as the fairy woman of the Blue Hills had asked.

The Coming of the Corn

In old times there dwelt on the shores of a great lake a mighty warrior. His people had all been driven far away inland by hostile tribes, but he remained behind to roam over the islands in the lake and to send his people word of any approaching attack. His wife was dead; she had been killed by treacherous foes. He had two little boys, and he kept them with him in his wanderings by the lake. He was a great magician as well as a man of great strength and he had no fear in his heart. The islands in the lake were haunted by spirits or 'manitous', but the man was not afraid of them, and with his boys he paddled his canoe up and down, watching for signs of his foes. Each night he landed in a cove and pulled his canoe far up among the trees, and slept in the woods out of the sight of travellers. But he found it very hard to get game and fish, and often his boys were very hungry.

One morning at dawn of day he rose and went to find food for breakfast. He left his little boys asleep under the trees. He walked through the forest until he came suddenly upon a wide and open red plain. There was not a tree or a rock or a blade of grass upon it. He set out across the plain and, when he reached the middle of it, he met a small man with a red feather in his cap.

'Where are you going?' said the little man.

'I am going across the plain to the woods on the other side,' said the man. 'My boys are hungry without food and I am looking for game.'

'How strong are you?' said the little man.

'I am as strong as the human race,' said the man, 'but no stronger.'

'My name is Red Plume,' said the little man. 'We must wrestle. If you should make me fall, say to me "I have thrown you." If you should overcome me, you will never want for food, for you will have other nourishment than fish and game.'

They smoked their pipes for a long while and then they wrestled. They wrestled for a long time. The warrior was growing weak, for the little man was very strong. But at last he threw Red Plume down and cried: 'I have thrown you.' And at once the little man disappeared. When the warrior looked on the ground where his opponent had fallen, he saw only a crooked thing like an acorn with a red tassel on it. He picked it up and looked at it, and as he looked, a voice from it said: 'Take off my outside covering; split me into many parts, and throw the parts over the plain; scatter every bit of me; throw my spine near the woods. Then in a month come back to the plain.' The warrior did as he was told and then went back to his boys. On the way he killed a rabbit and cooked it for breakfast. He did not tell his boys what he had seen.

At the end of a month he went alone again to the plain. In the place where he had scattered the pieces of the strange object, he found blades of strange grass peeping green above the ground. And where he had thrown the pieces of the spine near the wood, little pumpkins were growing.

He did not tell his boys what he had found. All summer he watched for his foes, and in the autumn he went again to the place where he had thrown down the man of the Red Plume. The plain was covered with Indian corn in the ear, and there were also pumpkins of great size near the woods. The corn was golden yellow, and red tassels grew from the top of the ears. He plucked some ears of corn and gathered some of the pumpkins and set out to find his boys. Then a voice spoke from the corn. He knew it at once to be the voice of the man of the Red Plume. It said: 'You have conquered me. If you had failed, you would still have lived, but often you would

have hungered as before. Henceforth you shall never want for food, for when game and fish are scarce you will have bread. And I will never let the human race lack food if they keep me near them.' So corn came to the Indians in olden times, and never afterwards did they want for food.

When the man came to his boys, he told them what he had found. He ground some of the corn between stones and made bread from the meal, and he cooked a pumpkin and ate it. Then he thought of his poor old father and mother far away beyond the hills, perhaps without food. So that night he took his boys and travelled far through the forest until he found his parents. He told them of his meeting with the man of the Red Plume and of the coming of the corn. And he brought them back with him to the 'manitou' islands near the shores of the great lake. And ever afterwards the fields were fruitful and corn was abundant and never failed in the land where Red Plume fell.

The Boy Who Overcame the Giants

Once long ago, before the white men came to Canada, an orphan boy was living alone with his uncle. He was not very happy, for he had to work very hard, and tasks more fitted for a man's shoulders than for a boy's were often placed upon him. When his parents died and left him without brother or sister, his uncle took him to his own home because there was no one else to take care of him. But he treated him very cruelly and often he wished to get rid of him. It mattered not how well the boy did his work or how many fish and animals he caught, his uncle was never satisfied, and often he beat the boy harshly and with little cause. The boy would have run away but he did not know where to go, and he feared to wander alone in the dark forest. So he decided to endure his hardships as best he could.

Now it happened that in a distant village near the sea there lived a Chief who was noted far and wide for his cruelty. He had a wicked temper, and he was known to have put many people to death for no reason whatsoever. More than all else, he hated boastfulness, and he had scanty patience with anyone who was vain of his own strength. He pledged himself always to humble the proud and to debase the haughty. The boy's uncle had heard of this wicked ruler, and he said: 'Here is a chance for me to get rid of the boy. I will tell lies about him to the Chief.'

It chanced just at this time that three giants came into the Chief's territory. Where they came from, no man knew, but they dwelt in a large cave near the sea, and they caused great havoc and destruction in all the land. They ate up great stores of food and all the little children they could lay their hands on. The Chief used every means to get rid of the giants, but without success. Night after night his best warriors went to the cave by the ocean to seek out the giants, but not a man returned. A piece of birch bark bearing a picture of a warrior with an arrow in his heart, found the next day at the Chief's door, always told him of the warrior's fate. And the giants continued their cruel work, for no one could stop them.

Soon all the country was in great terror. The Chief wondered greatly what was to be done. At last he thought: 'I will give my daughter to the man who can rid me of these pests.' His daughter was his only child and she was very beautiful, and he knew that many suitors would now appear to seek her hand, for, although the task was dangerous, the prize was worth while. When the wicked uncle in the distant village heard of it, he thought: 'Now I can get rid of the boy, for I will tell the Chief that the boy says he can kill the giants.' So, taking his nephew with him, he went to the Chief's house and begged to see him. 'Oh, Chief,' he said, 'I have a boy who boasts that before many days have passed he can free your land from the giants.' And the Chief said: 'Bring him to me.' The man said: 'Here he is.' The Chief was surprised when he saw the small boy, and he said: 'You have promised that you can rid my land of giants. Now we shall see if you can do it. If you succeed you may have my daughter. If you fail, you will die. If you escape from the giants, I will kill you myself. I hate vain boasters, and they shall not live in my land.'

The boy went and sat by the ocean and cried as hard as he could. He thought that he would surely die, for he was very small and he had no means of killing the giants. But as he sat there an old woman came along. She came quietly and quickly out of the grey mist of the sea. And she said: 'Why are you crying?' And the boy said: 'I am crying because I am forced to attack the giants in the cave, and if I cannot kill them I shall surely die,' and he cried louder than before. But the old woman, who was the good fairy of the sea, said: 'Take this bag and this knife and these three little stones that I will give you, and when you go tonight to the giants' cave, use them as I tell you and all will be well.' She gave him three small white stones and a small knife, and a bag like the bladder of a bear, and she taught him their use. Then she disappeared into the grey mist that hung low on the ocean and the boy never saw her again.

The boy lay down on the sand and went to sleep. When he awoke, the moon was shining, and far along the coast in the bright light he could see an opening in the rocks which he knew was the entrance to the giants' cave. Taking his bag and his knife and the three little stones, he approached it cautiously with a trembling heart. When he reached the mouth of the cave he could hear the giants snoring inside, all making different noises, louder than the roar of the sea. Then he remembered the old woman's instructions. He tied the bag inside his coat so that the mouth of it was close to his chin. Then he took one of the stones from his pocket. At once it grew to immense size, so heavy that the boy could scarcely hold it. He threw it at the biggest giant with great force, and it hit him squarely on the head. The giant sat up staring wildly and rubbing his brow. He kicked his younger brother, who was lying beside him, and said in great anger: 'Why did you strike me?' 'I did not strike you,' said his brother. 'You struck me on the head while I slept,' said the giant, 'and if you do it again I will kill you.' Then they went to sleep again.

When the boy heard them snoring loudly again, he took a second stone from his pocket. At once it grew great in size and the boy hurled it with great force at the biggest giant. Again the giant sat up staring wildly and rubbing his head. But this time he did not speak. He grasped his axe, which was lying beside him, and killed his brother with a blow. Then he went to sleep again. When the boy heard him snoring, he took the third stone from his pocket. At once it grew to great size and weight, and he hurled it with all his force at the giant. Again the giant sat up with great staring eyes, rubbing the lump on his head. He was now in a great rage. 'My brothers have plotted to kill me,' he yelled, and seizing his axe he killed his remaining brother with a blow. Then he went to sleep, and the boy slipped from the cave, first gathering

up the three stones, which were now of their usual small size.

The next morning, when the giant went to get water from the stream, the boy hid in the trees and began to cry loudly. The giant soon discovered him and asked: 'Why are you crying?' 'I have lost my way,' said the boy. 'My parents have gone and left me. Please take me into your service, for I would like to work for such a kind handsome man and I can do many things.' The giant was flattered by what the boy said, and, although he liked to eat little children, he thought: 'Now that I am alone I ought to have a companion, so I will spare the boy's life and make him my servant.' And he took the boy back to his cave, and said: 'Cook my dinner before I come home. Make some good stew, for I shall be very hungry.'

When the giant went into the forest the boy prepared the evening meal. He cut up a great store of deer meat and put it in a large pot bigger than a hogshead and made a good meat stew. When the giant came home in the evening he was very hungry, and he was well pleased to see the big pot filled with his favourite food. He seated himself on one side of the pot and the boy seated himself on the other side, and they dipped their spoons into the big dish. And the boy said: 'We must eat it all up so that I can clean the pot well, and ready for the corn mush we will have for breakfast.' The stew was very hot, and to cool it before he ate it the giant blew his breath on what he dipped out. But the boy poured his own share into the bag under his coat, and said: 'Why can't you eat hot food—a big man like you? In my country men never stop to cool their stew with their breath.' Now the giant could not see very well, for his eyesight was not very good, and the cave was dark, and he did not notice the boy putting the stew in the bag so quickly. He thought the boy was eating it. And he was shamed by the boy's taunts because he was so much larger than the boy, so he ate up the hot stew at once in great gulps and burned his throat badly. But he was too proud to stop or to complain.

When they had eaten half the potful, the giant said: 'I am full. I think I have had enough.' 'No, indeed,' said the boy, 'you must show that you like my cooking. In my country men eat much more than that,' and he kept on eating. The giant was not to be outdone by a boy, so he fell to eating again, and they did not stop until they had consumed the whole potful of stew. But the boy had poured his share into the bag and when they had finished he was swelled out to an immense size. The giant could scarcely move, he had eaten so much, and he said: 'I have eaten too much. I feel very full and I have a great pain in

my belly.' And the boy said: 'I do not feel very comfortable myself, but I have a way to cure pains.' So saying, he took his little knife and thrust it gently into the
side of the bag and the stew oozed out and he was soon
back to his normal size. The giant wondered greatly at
the sight, but the boy said: 'It is a way they have in my
country after they have had a great feast.' 'Does the knife
not hurt?' asked the giant. 'No, indeed,' said the boy, 'it
brings great relief.' 'My throat is very sore,' said the
giant, for the hot stew had burned him. 'You will soon
feel better,' said the boy, 'if you will do as I have done.'
The giant hesitated to do this, but soon he felt so un-
comfortable that he could bear it no longer. He saw that

the boy was feeling quite well, so he took his long knife and plunged it into his stomach. 'Strike hard,' said the boy, 'or it will do you no good.' The giant plunged the knife in to the hilt, and in an instant he fell dead.

Then the boy took the stones and the bag and the knife which the Woman of the Mist had given him and went and told the Chief what he had done. The Chief sent his messengers to the cave to make sure that the boy spoke the truth. Sure enough, they found the three giants lying dead. When they told the Chief what they had seen, he said to the boy: 'You may have my daughter as your wife.' But the boy said: 'I do not want your daughter. She is too old and fat. I want only traps to catch fish and game.' So the Chief gave the boy many good traps, and he went into a far country to hunt game, and there he lived happily by himself. And his wicked uncle never saw him again. But the land was troubled no more by giants because of the boy's great deeds.

The Dance of Death

Once long ago there lived on the banks of a beautiful Canadian river a powerful Indian tribe. In the tribe was a very handsome young man, very brave and a great hunter. He was loved by a young Indian girl who was likewise very beautiful. But the young man repulsed her love. He was a great warrior; he was busy getting ready for the autumn and winter hunt and he had little time for such nonsense as love. He frankly told the young girl that he did not love her and that she must follow him no more.

Now the young girl was very angry, for she was proud and beautiful and of a high temper, and she was little used to have her desires refused. She had a very strange power which the Spirit of the Night had placed in her cradle at her birth. It was a power by which she could do great harm to mankind, but she had never used it in all her life. But now in her anger she said to the young man as he went away with his comrades: 'You may go;

but you will never return as you go.' The young man gave no heed to her words; he neither cared for her nor feared her, and with a merry heart he went his way with his companions.

One day many weeks later, when they were far away in the north country in the land of ice and snow, the young man became suddenly ill. Then he went raging mad with what the Indians call the wild 'madness of the woods'. The girl's strange power was upon him. In the band of hunters was the young man's older brother, a very strong and powerful man. He knew what ailed his brother. He went to the river and sang the strange weird song that calls the Evil Spirit of the Stream to man's assistance. Now this was a very dangerous thing to do, for the Spirit of the Stream had no love for cowards; but the man, being brave, had no fear, as he wished to save his brother's life. After the usual custom, he dared the Evil Spirit of the Stream to come to him. Soon the monster appeared in answer to the challenge, its great eyes shining like fire on the water and its horns rising above the surface. It asked the man what he wished, and the man answered: 'I wish you to help me; I wish my brother to be in his right mind again and free from the maiden's wicked power.' Then the monster said: 'You may have what you wish if you are not afraid,' and the man said that he feared nothing. And the monster asked: 'Do you fear me?' And the man said: 'No.' 'Then,' said the monster, 'take hold of my horns and scrape them with your knife.' The man did as he was told, and he scraped and scraped until he had taken a handful of powder from the monster's horns.

The monster wondered at the man's bravery and said:

'Go to your camp now. Put half the scrapings into a cup of water and give it to your brother to drink; put the other half in another cup of water and give it to the maiden to drink when you go back home, and all will be well.' Then the Indian returned to the camp and did as the monster had told him, and his brother drank the powdered water and soon got back his senses and his strength.

When the hunt was ended, the band returned home. It was night in the springtime when they reached their village; the snow had already left the ground and the trees were in bud. In a great tent in the village the annual spring dance was in progress, and all the people of the place were gathered. Among them was the maiden lover dancing merrily with the rest. None of the hunting band entered the tent, but they watched the dance from outside the door. The elder brother had mixed a drink as the Evil Spirit of the Stream had told him, by placing the remainder of the powder in a cup of water. And he stood at the door waiting for his chance to give it to the girl. The night was hot and still, and he knew that the dancers would soon grow warm and thirsty. At last the maiden lover came to the door to breathe the cool night air. The man passed her the cup, and, without looking at him or knowing him, she took it and gladly drained it dry because of her great thirst; then she went back to the dance.

Then a very strange shadow came upon her. When she began to dance she was a young and beautiful girl, the loveliest of all the maidens in the land. But after she had drunk the magic cup she grew gradually older. Her friends noticed the change and stood rooted with terror.

The tales of their parents came back to their memories; they knew that the girl was now passing through the Dance of Death from which no power could save her.

Their fears were well founded. At each turn of the dance, a year was added to the girl's life; the colour faded slowly from her cheeks; her shoulders slowly stooped; wrinkles appeared upon her face; her hands trembled as if palsied; her feet lost their nimbleness and her tread was no longer light. She was growing old in the Dance of Death. Yet she was unconscious of it all, and her life ebbed away without her knowing it. At last she reached the end of the room, tottering to the music of the dance; but old age was now upon her and she fell dead upon the floor. Her power over the young man was forever ended, for the Spirit of the Stream had brought about the Dance of Death.

'She will trouble you no more,' said the elder Indian to his brother as he gazed upon the shrunken face and form. 'Her dance is forever ended.'

The people wondered greatly at the strange happening, and their merry-making was hushed; and since that day the Indians in silent fear still point you on the river to the scene of the Dance of Death.

The Song-Bird and the Healing Waters

Once when the snow lay very deep on the ground and the days were grey with frost, there was great sorrow in an Indian village. A dreadful plague had come upon the place and had carried away many of the people. Neither old nor young were proof against its ravages, and the weak and the strong fell helpless before its power. The people tried every means to get rid of the plague, but they had no success. And they prayed to all their good spirits to help them, but no help came. In the tribe was a young warrior who had lost his parents and all his brothers and sisters because of the dreaded disease. Now his young wife fell sick, and he was in great sorrow, for he thought that she would soon follow his parents into the Land of the Shadows. And so he went about in great fear, not knowing when the end would come.

One day he met an old woman in the forest. 'Why do you look so sorrowful?' she asked him. 'I am sad because, my young wife is going to die,' he answered. 'The plague will carry her off like the others.' But the old woman said: 'There is something that will save your wife from death. Far away in the east is a bird of sweet song which dwells close to the Healing Waters. Go until you find it. It will point you to the spring, the waters of which alone can heal.' And the young man said: 'I must find the Healing Waters. Wherever they may be upon the earth, I must find them.' So he went home and said goodbye to his friends and set out eastward on his quest.

All the next day he searched eagerly for the Waters, listening always for the bird of the sweet song. But he found nothing. The snow lay deep in the forest and he moved along with difficulty. He met a rabbit in his path and he said: 'Tell me where I shall find the Healing Spring?' But the rabbit scurried away over the snow and made no answer. Then he asked a bear, but he met with the same rebuff. Thus for many days and nights he wandered on, crossing rivers and climbing steep hills, but always without success.

Then one day he emerged from the snow country and came to a land where the airs were warmer and where little streams were flowing. Suddenly he came upon the body of a dead man lying across his path. He stopped and buried the body, for he thought that it was not right to leave it lying bare upon the ground for the birds to peck at. That night as he went along in the moonlight he met a fox in his path. 'Hello,' said the fox. 'What are you looking for so late at night in the forest?' And he answered: 'I am looking for the bird of the sweet song who will show me the way to the Healing Waters.' And the fox said: 'I am the spirit of the man you buried yesterday by the forest path, and in return for your kindness to me

I shall do a kindness to you. You have always been good to the animals and the birds, and you have never killed them needlessly nor when you did not require them for clothing or for food. And you have always been careful of the flowers and the trees and you have often protected them from harm. So now they want to be good to you, and I am going to guide you. But first you must rest, for you are tired from your long journey.'

Then the young man lay down to sleep and the fox stood guard beside him. As he slept he dreamed. And in his dream he saw his wife, pale and thin and worn, and as he looked he heard her singing a song of wonderful melody. Then he heard a waterfall rippling near him and it said: 'Seek me, O warrior, and when you find me your wife shall live, for I am the Healing Waters.' In the morning the fox led him but a short distance through the forest, and on the branch of a tree he heard a bird singing a song of wonderful melody, just as he had heard in his dream of the night before. He knew now that this was the bird of the sweet song of which the old woman in the forest had spoken. Then, as he listened, he heard the sound of a waterfall rippling not far away. He searched for it, but he could not find it. And Fox said: 'You must seek it; you must not despair. It will not come to you unless you search.' So he searched again, and soon he thought he heard a voice speaking beneath his feet. 'Release us,' it called, 'set us free and your wife and your people shall be saved.' He seized a sharp stick and dug rapidly into the earth where he had heard the voice. He worked eagerly and quickly, and he had not dug far when the spring gushed forth and boiled upwards carrying to the world its healing power. And the young man knew that at last he had found the cure for his ills. He plunged into the spring and bathed himself in the water, and all his weariness left him and he was strong again.

Then the young man moulded from the soft earth a large pot. He baked it in the fire until it was quite hard. 'Now', said the fox spirit, 'I will leave you. Your kindness has been rewarded. You will need me no more, for you have found the Healing Waters.' And he disappeared as mysteriously as he had come. The young man filled his clay pot with the sparkling water and hastened back to

his home, running through the forest with the speed of the wind because of his renewed strength.

When he reached his native village, the people met him with sad faces, for the plague was still raging, and they told him that his young wife was about to pass to the Land of the Shadows. But he hurried to his home, and he forced some of the Healing Waters between his wife's parched lips and bathed her hands and her brow until she fell into a deep slumber. He watched by her side until she awoke, and when sleep left her she was well again. Then with his Healing Waters he cured all the people in the village, and the cruel plague left them and there was no more sickness in the land. And since that time no plague has spread among his tribe. In this way the Mineral Springs, the places of Healing Waters, came upon the earth, bearing health and happiness wherever they rise, and accompanied always by the songs of birds.

The Northern Lights

One autumn day in old times a woman and her infant son were lost in the Canadian woods. The woman was going back to her home from a long journey, and in some strange way she wandered from the path. The more she walked about, the more confused she became, and for many days she searched for the right road, but she could not find it. All the time she lived on berries and on the little food she carried.

At last she found a cave in the woods, and she decided to use it for a home. She had not been long in the cave when a large bear came in, and she knew then that she had taken refuge in a bear's den. She thought the bear would kill her and her child. But the bear was good. He looked upon them as his own kind and soon they all became friends. The bear hunted during the day, and each night he brought to the cave much meat, which the woman cooked. So they lived comfortably through the long winter.

After a time the woman's child grew to be a very strong boy. The bear taught him to wrestle, and after a few weeks' practice the boy could throw down his teacher. And the mother said: 'He will be a great warrior,' for she knew that his strength was more than human. When the boy grew large and strong enough to take care of his mother, they decided to try to find the way back to their old home. So one day they said goodbye to the bear, and set out on their journey. After many hardships and dangers they reached their native village where the people, who had thought them dead, received them with great rejoicing. The boy continued to grow in strength until the people said they had never seen anyone so powerful. There was no limit to his strength.

One day the boy said to his mother: 'I am going to travel far away until I find other men who are as strong as I am. Then my strength will be tested and I will come back to you.' His mother agreed that he should go, and one morning he set out on his strange journey.

He came to the bank of a river and there he saw a man standing not far ahead of him. As he looked, a large canoe came drifting down the river, filled with people. They had lost their paddles. One of the people called to the man on the bank and asked him to help them to land. The man put out a long pole and placed the end of it under the canoe, and lifted the canoe and all the people to the beach. 'There,' thought the boy, 'is a man as strong as I am.' Then the boy ran to the spot and picked up the canoe full of people and carried it up to the bank. He spoke to the man and told him of his own great strength. Then he said: 'We are two strong men. Let us go along together until we find a third man as strong as we are.' The man agreed, and he went along with the boy.

They travelled far that day, and in the afternoon they came to a country of high rocky hills. It was a lonely and silent place, and no people seemed to be living in it. At last they saw a man rolling a large stone up the side of a mountain. The stone was as large as a house, and the mountain was very steep, but the man rolled the stone up with ease. He had rolled it half-way up when the two strangers came along. The boy picked up the stone and threw it to the top of the mountain without difficulty. And the roller-man looked at them with great wonder. Then the boy told him of the strength of himself and his comrade, and said: 'We are three strong men. Let us go hunting together.' The man agreed, and the three went along together.

They built a house for themselves, to live in while they hunted. They agreed that only two of them should go away at once to hunt, and that the other should stay at home to look after the place and to prepare the evening meal. They decided that each should stay at home in his turn. The next day, the man of the river bank who had lifted the canoe stayed home. Towards evening he got ready for the coming of his comrades, and he cooked a good meal to have waiting for them. Just as he had finished cooking it, a small boy came in and asked for food. He was very small and worn and ragged, and the man pitied him and told him to eat what he wanted. The boy ate and ate until he had eaten all the food prepared for the three strong men. Then he went away and disappeared in the side of the mountain. When the two hunters came home they were very hungry, and they were cross when they heard that their meal had all been eaten up.

And they vowed vengeance on the little glutton who had taken all their food.

The next day it was the turn of the stone-rolling man to stay at home. In the evening he cooked a good meal for himself and his comrades. But before the hunters came home, the little boy came in again and asked for food. He looked so small and worn and he cried so bitterly that the man did not have the heart to send him away, and he told him to eat what he wanted. The boy ate and ate until not a scrap of food was left. Then he laughed and went out and disappeared in the mountain. When the two hunters came home, they were again very cross to find that their food had all been eaten up by a tiny boy.

The next day the strong boy stayed at home while the canoe-lifter and the stone-roller went hunting. In the evening the small boy came again, just as he had done on the two previous days. He wept and asked for food. The strong boy told him to eat what he wanted. He ate and ate as before, until he had eaten up the whole meal. Then he got up to go out. But the strong boy caught him and held him fast. There was a long struggle, for the tiny boy was very powerful and he was almost a match for the strong boy. But at last he was thrown down, and he pleaded for his life. The strong boy said he would spare him on condition that he would take him to his home. He wanted to see what kind of a place he lived in. And the small boy agreed.

Then the strong boy went with him to the side of the mountain. When they reached it, the little boy said: 'I am the servant of a terrible giant who has never been defeated in battle. I think you can overcome him. Take this stick and beat him with it, for it is the only thing that can give him pain.' Then he gave him a stick that lay on the ground, and they went on to the giant's cave in the side of the hill. When they went in, the giant sprang upon the strong boy. There was a long fight. It lasted for a whole day, and at last the strong boy overcame the giant and beat him dead with the magic stick. Then the little boy said: 'I will reward you for freeing me from my terrible master. I have three beautiful sisters, and you may have whichever one you want for your wife.'

He took the strong boy to his home in a cave far down in a valley on the other side of a mountain, and there they found the three beautiful girls. The strong boy took the youngest one for himself, and then he took the other two for his two comrades. When they came out of the cave, the strong boy found that they would have a very hard path to climb up the steep side of the mountain. Then luckily, as he thought, he saw his two strong comrades standing on the top of the high cliff far above him. They saw him and the three girls far below them. He called to them to let down a rope, and said: 'The three girls I have with me cannot climb the steep path. You must pull them up.' So the men above let down a strong cord and the strong boy sent up the two oldest girls first, one at a time.

Then, before sending up his own choice, the youngest, he thought he would test the loyalty of his comrades. They were standing far back from the top of the cliff, holding the rope, and they could not see the boy and the girl below. The boy tied a heavy stone to the end of the rope and called: 'I am going up next. Pull away.' The men pulled and pulled until they had drawn the weight near the top of the cliff. Then they cut the rope, and

down crashed the stone to the bottom of the cliff, where it broke into many pieces. The men above hoped that they had killed their comrade. They did not think that he had meant the two fairy wives for them, so they decided to kill him. But they were outwitted by the boy and the stone. 'That is a fine way to reward my kindness,' said the boy to his girl companion when he saw the stone in pieces on the rocks. As he spoke he looked up and saw the two fairy girls running away from the two men above, who were left all alone. Then with the magic help of the little boy, the girls' brother, the strong boy at once punished the two men by making them follow the girls. They followed them on and on, but they never found them. And they still follow them—they wander always, and they are never at rest.

Then the strong boy left the little boy behind him to look after himself, and he took his fairy wife and climbed up the path and went to live far away in the forest. For a time they lived very happily. One day the boy said: 'I am going back to my old home to see my people. You must wait here, and in a few days I shall come back.' The girl did not want him to go: she feared he would forget her; but he told her that he must go. Then she said: 'When you reach your home, a small black dog will meet you at the door. It will jump to lick your hand. But do not let it touch you. It is an evil spirit in disguise, and if it licks your hand you will forget all about me and you will not come back to me.'

The man promised to be on his guard, and he set out for his native place, leaving his wife behind him. Soon he reached his home, and as he opened the door, sure enough the black dog of which his wife had spoken jumped towards him. Before the strong boy could turn aside, the dog licked his hand as his wife had said. Then he forgot all about his old life in the forest; and he lived with never a thought of the fairy girl he had left behind him far away.

His wife waited long for him to come back. Then she knew that her husband had forgotten her because of the black dog, and late in the autumn she set out to find him. Soon she came to the place where he dwelt. It was morning, and she decided to hide until night and then go to his home. She went to a stream that ran beside the village and climbed into a tree that stretched out over the water. Near by was an old house in which an old man lived. The old man came to the brook for water and, as he bent down to fill his pail, he saw the face of the beautiful girl in the tree reflected in the stream. He called to her to come down from the tree. He had never seen a creature so lovely. He brought her to his tent and gave her food, and he told her that her husband had gone far up the river to hunt.

In the evening she went along the river to wait for her husband as he came home. When she saw him coming in his canoe, she sat on the bank of the stream and sang her magic song. It was a song of wonderful melody such as only fairy maidens can sing, and the sound went far over the water and charmed all who heard it. When her husband heard the song, he stopped to listen. He soon knew that the music was that of his fairy wife of the forest, for no one else on earth could sing so wonderful a song. Then his old life in the forest came back to his mind, with memories of the two strong men and the tiny boy and the three fairy girls. And he remembered his wife to whom he had promised to return. Then he paddled his canoe to the bank, and found his wife, and they were happy again.

It was a cold autumn night and the moon was full, and his wife said: 'We must not stay here. This is a wicked place where men forget. If you stay here, you will forget me again.' Then she shuddered when she thought that her husband might forget her again, and he shuddered when he thought that he might lose her again. And they continued to tremble in fear. Then she said: 'We must go to another land. It is a more beautiful land than this. It is the Land of Eternal Memory where men and women never forget those they loved. I know where it is. We will go to it.' Then she sang her magic song, and at once a great bird came through the air to where they sat. And, still trembling in fear lest they should forget each other, they sprang to the bird's back, and the bird carried them up to the sky. And there they were changed into Northern Lights.

And you can still see them, with their children around them, on autumn nights in the north country, beautiful in the northern sky. And they still tremble when they think of the Land of Forgetfulness they have left, and of the pain it caused them in the old days of their youth.

The Tobacco Fairy from the Blue Hills

A man and his wife and two little children were living long ago on the shores of a lake surrounded by large trees, deep in the Canadian forest. They lived very happily together, and as game was plentiful, they wanted for nothing. As the children grew up they became each day more beautiful and gentle, until the old women of the tribe said: 'They are too good and lovely for this world; their home is surely elsewhere in the west.' Before they grew to maturity a cruel plague spread over the land and carried them off with its ravages. Their mother was the next to go, slowly growing weaker and wasting away before the eyes of her husband, who was powerless to save her.

The man was now left alone upon the earth. The joy of his life had gone with his wife and children, and he went about in great loneliness and sorrow. Life was long to him and dreary, and often he wished that he too was dead. But at last he roused himself and said: 'I will go about doing good. I will spend my life helping others and perhaps in that way I can find peace.' So he worked hard and did all the good he could for the weaker and the poorer people of his tribe. He was held in high esteem by all the people of the village, and in their affection for him they all called him 'Grandfather'. He grew to be very old, and because of his good deeds he found great happiness. But he was still very solitary, and the days and evenings were long and lonely, and as he grew older and his work grew less, he found it hard to pass away the time, for he could only sit alone and dream of his vanished youth and of his absent friends.

One day he sat thinking by the lake. Many people of the village were around him, but as usual he sat alone. Suddenly a large flock of birds, looking like great black clouds, came flying from the blue hills in the distance toward the shore of the lake. They wheeled and circled about and hovered long over the trees, uttering strange cries. The people had never before seen such large birds, and they were much afraid and said: 'They are not ordinary creatures. They foreshadow some strange happening.' Suddenly one of the birds fluttered for an instant and fell slowly to the earth with an arrow in its breast. No one in the village had shot at the flock, and where the arrow had come from no man knew. The mystery frightened the people still more, and they looked to the old man for counsel, for they knew that he was very wise.

The fallen bird lay fluttering on the ground, seemingly in pain. The other birds circled about it for a short time, uttering loud cries. Then they screamed and called to each other and flew back to the distant blue hills, leaving the fallen bird behind them with the arrow sticking in its breast. The old man was not frightened by the sight. He said: 'I will go to the stricken bird. Perhaps I can heal its wound.' But the people, in great fear, said: 'Do not go, Grandfather. The bird will do you harm.' But the old man answered: 'It can do no harm to me. My work is ended and my life is almost done. My sky is dark, for I am full of sorrow, and with me it is already the twilight of time. I am alone in the world, for my kindred have gone. I am not afraid of death, for to me it would be very welcome. What matters it if I should die?' And he went to the stricken bird to see if he could help it.

As he went along, his path suddenly grew dark, but as he drew nearer, a bright flame suddenly swept down from the sky to the place where the bird was lying. There was a flash of fire, and when the old man looked he saw that the bird had been completely burned up. When he came to where it had lain, nothing but black ashes remained. He stirred up the ashes with his stick, and lying in the centre he found a large living coal of fire. As he looked at it, in a twinkling it disappeared, and in its place was a strange little figure like a little man, no bigger than his thumb. 'Hello, Grandfather,' it called, 'do not strike me, for I have been sent to help you.'

'Who are you?' asked the old man.

'I am one of the Little People from the distant blue hills,' said the tiny boy. Then the old man knew that the little fellow was one of the strange fairy people of the mountains of whom he had often heard. 'What do you want?' he asked.

'I have been sent to you with a precious gift,' answered

the little man. The old man wondered greatly, but he said nothing.

Then the fairy from the blue hills said: 'You are old and lonely. You have done many noble deeds, and you have always gone about bringing good to others. In that way you have found peace. And because of your good life, I have been sent to bring you more contentment. Your work is done, but your life is not yet ended, and you have still a long time to dwell upon the earth. You must live out your mortal course. You are longing always for your dead wife and children, and you are often thinking of your youth, and with you the days are long and time hangs heavy. But I have been sent to you with a gift that will help you to pass the time more pleasantly.'

Then the little man gave him a number of small seeds and said: 'Plant these at once, here, in the ashes from which I have just risen.' The old man did as he was told. At once the seeds sprouted and great leaves grew from them, and soon the place where the bird had been burned up became a large field of tobacco.

The fairy then gave him a large pipe and said: 'Dry these leaves and place them in this pipe and smoke them. You will have great contentment, and when you have nothing to do it will help you to pass the time away, and when no one is with you it will be a companion. And it will bring you many dreams of the future and of the past. And when the smoke curls upwards it will have for you many visions of those you loved, and you will see their faces in the smoke as you sit alone in the twilight.'

The old man was very thankful for the fairy's gift. But the little man said: 'Teach other old men how to use it so that they too may possess it and enjoy it.'

Then the fairy quickly disappeared, going towards the distant blue hills, and he was never seen in the village again. And with his pipe and his tobacco the old man went back to his dreaming with more contentment than before. In this way, tobacco was brought to the Indians in the old days.

Star-Boy and the Sun Dance

Once long ago when the Blackfeet Indians dwelt on the Canadian prairies, it happened that a band of the people were camped near the mountains. It was springtime, and warm winds blew over the prairies laden with the scent of wild flowers. One hot cloudless night two girls slept in the long prairie grass beside their tents with no covering but the sky. The elder awoke before dawn and saw the Morning Star just rising. Very beautiful and bright he looked in the clear morning air, with no smoke or dust to hide him. The girl looked long at the Star, and she had strange fancies, and imagined that he was her lover. At last she called her sister and said: 'Look at the Morning Star. He is bright and wise. I love the Morning Star, for he is more beautiful than man.'

One day in the autumn when the flowers were faded and the grass was yellow with age and the cool winds blew over the prairie and the birds were flying south, as the girl was returning home from a long walk she met

a young man on the trail. In his hair was a yellow plume, and in his hand a small shrub with a big spider-web hanging to it. He was very beautiful, and he wore fine clothes of soft skins, and the odour of his dress was that of the sweet-grass and the pine. As the girl drew aside from the trail to pass, he put forth his hand and stopped her. 'Stand aside,' she said, 'and let me pass.' But he answered: 'I am the Morning Star. One night in spring when the flowers were blooming I saw you sleeping in the long grass outside your tent, and I loved you. I heard you say you loved only me, and now I have come to ask you to come with me to the sky to the home of my father, the Sun, where we shall live together and you will have no more troubles nor cares. It is the Land of Little People, the Land of the Ever-Young, where all are happy like children, and no one ever grows old.' Then the girl remembered the hot cloudless night in the springtime when she slept in the tall grass, and she knew now that Morning Star was to be her husband.

And she said: 'I must first say goodbye to my father and mother.' But Morning Star said: 'There must be no leave-taking,' and he would not let her go home. He fastened his yellow plume in her hair, and gave her the shrub to hold. He told her to place her feet upon the lowest strand of the spider's web and to hold the uppermost strand in her hands. Then he told her to shut her eyes. After a brief time, when he asked her to open her eyes, they were in the sky.

They passed on to a large tent. Morning Star said: 'This is the home of my father and mother, the Sun and the Moon,' and he asked her to enter. As it was day, the Sun was away on his long journey, but the Moon was at home and she welcomed the girl as her son's bride. And the girl lived happy in the Star country with her husband, and she learned many wonderful things.

Not far from her home, near the tent of the Spider Man who weaved webs, a large turnip was growing about which she wondered greatly. But the Moon, seeing her wonder, said: 'You may dig any roots that grow in the sky, but I warn you not to dig up the large turnip. If you do, unhappiness will follow you.'

After a time a son was born to the girl, and everywhere the girl went she carried the child. She called him Star-Boy. She often saw the large turnip near the tent of the Spider Man who weaved webs, but mindful of the Moon's warning, she was afraid to touch it.

One day, however, her wonder overcame her, and she decided to see what was underneath the turnip. She tried to pull it up, but it stuck fast and she was unable to move it. Then two large cranes flying from the east came to her aid, and, catching the turnip with their long bills, they moved it from side to side, loosened it, and pulled it up. The girl looked through the hole and saw the earth far beneath her. It was the same hole through which Morning Star had brought her to the sky. She looked long through the hole and she saw the camps of her people, the Blackfeet, on the plains far below. What she saw was well known to her. It was summer on the prairies. The men were playing games; the women were tanning skins or gathering berries on the rolling hills. She grew very lonely as she watched, for she wanted to be back on the green prairies with her own people, and when she turned away to go home she was crying bitterly.

When she reached home, Morning Star and his mother the Moon were waiting for her. Morning Star at once knew from her face what had happened, and he said: 'You have pulled up the sacred turnip!' When she did not answer, the Moon said: 'I warned you not to dig it up because I love Star-Boy and I do not wish to part with him.' It was day, and the Sun was away on his long journey. When he came home in the evening, he asked what was the matter with his daughter, for she looked sad and troubled. And the girl answered that she was lonely because she had looked down that day upon her people on the plains. Then the Sun was very angry, and said to Morning Star: 'If she has disobeyed, she must go back to her people. She cannot live here.' Morning Star and the Moon pleaded with the Sun to let her remain, but the Sun said that it was better that she go back to the prairies, for she would no longer be happy in the sky.

Then Morning Star led the girl to the house of the Spider Man who had weaved the web that had drawn her up to the sky. He placed Star-Boy on her breast and wrapped around them both a bright robe. Then he bade them farewell, saying: 'We will let you down where your people on the plains can see you as you fall.' Then the Spider Man with his web let her down as she had come, through the hole in the sky.

It was a hot, still evening in midsummer when the girl returned to her people. Many of the people were outside their tents, and they saw a bright light in the northern sky. They watched it slowly drop until it reached the ground. They thought it was a shooting star. They ran to the place where the bright light fell, and there they found a strange bundle inside of which were the woman and her child. Her parents knew her, and she returned with them to their home and lived with them. But she was never happy. Often she took Star-Boy to the top of a high hill in the west, where she sat and mourned for her home in the sky. And daily she watched Morning Star rise from the plains. Once she begged him to take her back to the country of the stars, but he answered: 'You disobeyed, and therefore I cannot take you back. Your sin is the cause of your sorrow, and it has brought great trouble to you and your people.'

So the Star Woman lived alone and unhappy upon the earth because she had disobeyed. After a time she died, and her son, Star-Boy, was left alone. Although born in the home of the Sun, he was very poor. He had little of the world's goods and but few clothes to wear. He was so timid that he never played with other children, and he lived much by himself. On his face was a strange scar which became more marked as he grew older. Because of this and his shy and timid ways, he was laughed at by everybody; other boys stoned him and abused him and called him Scarface.

When Star-Boy became a man he loved a girl of his own people. She was very beautiful and many young men wanted to marry her, but she refused them all. She told Star-Boy that she would not marry him until he removed the strange scar from his face. He was much troubled by this answer and he talked about it to the old medicine-woman who knew many things. The medicine-woman told him that the scar had been placed on his face by the Sun and that only the Sun himself could take it off. So he decided to go to the home of the Sun.

He went across the prairies and over the mountains for many days, meeting many dangers and suffering great hardships. At last he came to the Great Water in the West —the Pacific Ocean. For three days and nights he lay on the sand fasting and praying to the Sun God. On the evening of the fourth day he saw a bright trail leading across the water to the west. He ran along this path across the water until he came at last to the home of the Sun, where he hid himself and waited. Early next morning the Sun came out of his tent, ready for his day's journey. He saw Star-Boy but he did not know him, for Star-Boy had grown since he left the country of the stars. The Sun was angry when he saw a creature from earth and, calling his wife, the Moon, he said: 'We will kill him, for he comes from a good-for-nothing race.' But the Moon, being kind, prevented it and saved the boy's life. Then Morning Star, the boy's father, handsome and bright, came from his tent. He recognized his child, and, after the usual fashion in the sky, he brought dried sweet-grass and burned it so that the smoke curled around the boy and cleansed him from the dust of the earth. Then he brought him to his father and mother, the Sun and the Moon, and told them who the boy was. And Star-Boy told his story of his long journey, and of the marriage refusal of the girl he loved because of the scar on his face. And they took pity on him and promised to help him.

Star-Boy lived in the home of the Sun and Moon with Morning Star. Once he went hunting and killed seven large birds which had threatened the life of his father. He gave four of the dead birds to the Sun and three to the Moon. And the Sun, glad to be rid of these pests, resolved to pay him well for his work. As a reward, he took the scar from his face, as the medicine-woman had said. And he made him his messenger to the Blackfeet people on the Canadian plains, and promised that if they would give a festival in his honour once a year, he would heal their sick. The festival was to be known as the Sun Dance. He taught Star-Boy the secrets of the dance and the songs to be used in it so that he could tell his people. And he gave him two raven feathers to wear as a sign that he came from the Sun, and a very wonderful robe. And he gave him a magic flute and a wonderful song with which he could charm the heart of the girl he loved.

So Star-Boy returned to his people, the Blackfeet of the plains, running along by the Milky Way, the short, bright path to the earth. When he had taught them the secret of the Sun Dance, he married the girl he loved, and the Sun took them back to live with him in the sky. And he made him bright and beautiful, just like his father, Morning Star, and gave him work to do. Sometimes the father and son can be seen together in the sky; the people of earth sometimes call the father Venus, and

the son Jupiter, but the Indians call them Morning Star
and Little Morning Star. And since that time, once a
year, the Blackfeet of the plains hold the Sun Dance that
their sick may all be healed, as it was promised to Star-
Boy by the Sun God in the old days.

The Mouse and the Sun

Long before the white men came to Canada, and when
the animals ruled the earth, a little boy and his sister
lived alone on the Canadian plains. Their father and
mother died when the children were very young. The
children had no relations, and they were left to look after
themselves. They lived many miles from other people;
indeed, they had never seen any people but their parents,
they lived so far away. The boy was very small; he was
no bigger than a baby. The girl was large and strong,
and she had to provide food for both of them and do all
the work in the house. She had to take care of her
brother, and she took him with her wherever she went
so that no harm would come to him. She made him a bow
and a number of arrows to play with. One day in winter
she went out to gather wood for the fire. She took her
little brother with her. She told him to hide while she
walked farther on. She said: 'You will soon see a flock of
snow-birds passing near you if you watch. Shoot one of

them and bring it home.' The snow lay deep on the plains, and many snow-birds were flying around looking for food. The boy tried to shoot them, but his aim was not good and he was unable to hit any of them. When his sister came back to him he had no bird and he was very much ashamed. But his sister said: 'Never mind. Do not be discouraged. You will have better luck tomorrow.'

The next day the girl took her brother with her again when she went to gather wood. She left him behind at the place where he had hidden himself the day before. Again the snow-birds came flying past, searching for food. The boy shot several arrows at them, and at last he killed one. When his sister came back to him he showed her the bird. He was pleased with his success, and he said: 'I shall try to kill one each day. You must skin them, and when we have enough skins, I shall make a coat from them'. And his sister promised to do as he wished. Each day the boy went with his sister and waited for the snow-birds to fly past. And each day he killed one and took it home. They skinned the birds and dried the skins. Soon the boy had enough bird skins to make a coat, for he was very small (a few bird skins made his coat). His sister sewed the skins together and the boy put on the coat. He was very proud of it.

One day the boy said to his sister: 'Sister, we are all alone in the world. We have never seen any other people except our father and mother. Are there any other people on the earth?' His sister told him that she had heard from her mother that other people lived far away to the east beyond the mists of the prairie, and that others, from whom his mother had come, lived away to the west beyond the distant hills. The boy said: 'I should like to see

my mother's people if they are anywhere on the earth.'
So one day when his sister was away he put on his bird-
skin coat and took his bow and arrows and set out towards the distant hills to see if he could find his mother's
people.

It was springtime in the north country. The sun had
melted the snow, and little streams were flowing and
little blades of grass had begun to peep above the ground.
But the earth was soft and wet, and the day was hot, and
warm winds blew over the plains. The boy walked for a
long time. By the time the sun was high up in the sky, he
was very tired, for he was very small. He came to a dry
knoll and lay down to rest. Soon he fell asleep. As he
slept, the sun beat down upon him. It was so hot that it
singed his bird-skin coat; then the coat shrank and shrank
in the heat until it was only a small patch on his back.
When he awoke and stretched himself, he burst his coat
in many places, it had grown so tight. He was very cross
when he saw how the sun had ruined his coat. He shook
his fist at the sun and said: 'I will have vengeance; you
need not think you are too high to escape me. I will
punish you yet.' He decided that without his coat he
could not go any further to seek his mother's people, and
at evening he returned home.

When he reached home, he showed his sister his ruined
coat. He was very sad, and for weeks he would scarcely
eat a bite. And all the time he spoke bitterly of the sun.
His sister tried to comfort him. She told him that next
winter when the snow-birds came flying south again, he
could kill more of them and she would make him another
coat. But for a long time he would not be comforted. At
last he roused himself. He asked his sister to make him a

snare, for he was going to catch the sun. She made him a snare from a buffalo-hide cord, but he told her that it would not do. Then she cut off some of her long black hair and from it she made a braided noose. The boy said that it would do very well. Then he set out to catch the sun.

He travelled many days until he came to the Great Water in the east. It was summer in the north country and the sun rose early. The boy placed his snare just where the sun would strike the land when he rose at dawn out of the sea, and he watched from a distance. Sure enough in the morning, just as the sun rose out of the sea and came above the earth, he was caught in the snare and held fast. The sun could not rise; he was held fast to the earth. The boy was quite pleased with his success. 'Now,' he said, 'I have punished the sun for ruining my bird-skin coat.' And he returned to his home on the plains.

That day there was no light upon the earth: it was twilight in all the land. The animals were in great fear and wonder. The birds fled to their nests, and only the owl came out to look for food. At last the animals and the birds called a council to see what they could do. They found that the sun was tied to the earth by a snare. They decided that someone must go up close to the sun and cut the cord that held him. It was a very dangerous task, for the heat was very great and any one who tried to cut the cord would perhaps be burned to death. So they drew lots to see who should go.

The lot fell to Woodpecker. And Woodpecker went up and picked at the cord with his bill. He tried hard to cut it, but it was a strong braid of woman's hair and it could

not be cut easily. Woodpecker picked and picked at it
for a long time. At last his head was so badly burned that
he could stand the heat no longer and he had to fly away
without cutting the cord. His head was red from the
great heat. And ever since, poor Woodpecker has had
a red head because the sun singed him when he tried to
set him free.

Then the animals called for a volunteer to undertake
the task of cutting the snare. Mouse was at that time the
largest and strongest animal in the world, and he thought
that, because of his great strength, it was his duty to attempt the hard and dangerous task. So he set out. When

he reached the snare, he tried to cut the cord with his teeth, but the cord was strong and could not be cut easily. The heat was very great. Mouse would have run away, but he was so big and strong that he was ashamed to leave the task, for he thought that the smaller animals would laugh at him. So he stuck to his work and sawed the cord with his teeth, one hair at a time. Soon his back began to burn and scorch and smoke. But he stuck to his task. Then he began to melt away because of the great heat, and the whole top of his body was burned to ashes. But still he stuck to his task for a long time, cutting hair after hair. Finally he cut the last hair. The snare parted, and the sun was at last free to continue his day's journey and give light to the world. And the animals and birds rejoiced greatly over the success of Mouse.

But poor Mouse had melted almost entirely away in the great heat. When he went up to the snare, he was the largest animal in the world; when he came down, he was the smallest. And his back was burned to ashes. And ever since, Mouse has been the smallest animal in the world, and his coat has always been the colour of grey ashes, because he was scorched when freeing the sun from a snare in the old days.

The Giant with the Grey Feathers

Once long ago, when the Blackfeet Indians dwelt on the Canadian plains, there was a great famine in all the land. For many months no buffaloes were killed, and there was no meat to be had at any price. One by one the old people dropped off because of a lack of food, and the young children died early because there was no nourishment, and there was great sorrow everywhere. Only the strong women and the stronger warriors remained alive, but even they gradually grew weaker because of the pinch of the hunger sent into the land by famine. At last the Chief of the tribe prayed that the Great Chieftain of the Indians might come into his territory to tell the people what to do to save themselves.

The Great Chief was at that time far away in the south country where the warm winds were blowing and the flowers were blooming. But one night he heard the Chief's prayer borne to him on the winds, and he hastened northward, for he knew that his people on the plains were somehow in dire distress. Soon he arrived at the village of the hungry tribe. 'Who has called me here?' he asked. 'It was I,' answered the Chief. 'My people are all starving because there are no buffaloes in the country, and if you had not come we should soon have all perished.' Then the Great Chief looked upon his people and he noticed that the old folks and the little children had disappeared; only a few children were left and they had pinched cheeks and sunken eyes. And he took pity on them and said: 'There is a great thief not far distant. He is probably a wicked giant and he has driven all the buffaloes away. But I will find him and soon you shall have food.' And the people were all comforted, for they knew that the Great Chief would keep his word.

Then the Chief took with him the young Chief's son and set out on his quest. The people wanted to go with him, but he said: 'No, we shall go alone. It is a dangerous duty, and it is better that, if need be, two should die in the attempt than that all should perish.' They journeyed westwards across the prairies towards the Great Water in the west, and as they went, the youth prayed to the Sun and the Moon and the Morning Star to send them success. Soon they came to the rolling foot-hills covered with sweet-grass and scrubby pine. But still they saw no signs of buffalo. At last they reached a narrow stream, on the bank of which they saw a house with smoke from the chimney. 'There is the cause of all our troubles,' said the Chief. 'In that house dwells the giant buffalo-thief and his wife. They have driven all the animals from the prairies until not one is left. My magic power tells me it is so!' Then by his magic power he changed his companion into a sharp-pointed straight stick, while he himself took the shape of a dog, and they lay on the ground and waited.

Soon the giant and his wife and their little son came along. The boy patted the dog on the head, and said: 'See what a nice dog I have found? He must be lost. May I take him home?' His father said: 'No, I do not like his looks. Do not touch him.' The boy cried bitterly, for he had long hoped for a dog of his own, and his mother pleaded for him so hard that at last the giant father said: 'Oh, very well. Have your own way, but no good can come of it.' The woman picked up the stick and said: 'I will take this nice straight stick along with me. I can dig roots with it to make medicine.' So they all went to the giant's house, the giant frowning angrily, the woman carrying the stick, and the boy leading the dog.

The next morning the giant went out and soon came back with a fat young buffalo, all skinned and ready for cooking. They roasted it on a spit over the fire and had a good meal. The boy fed some meat to the dog, but his father, when he saw what the boy was doing, beat him soundly, and said: 'Have I not told you the dog is an evil thing? You must not disobey me.' But again the woman pleaded for her boy, and the dog was fed. That night, when all the world was asleep, the dog and the stick changed back to their human form and had a good supper of what was left of the buffalo meat. And the Chief said to the youth: 'The giant is the buffalo-thief who keeps the herds from coming to the prairies. It is useless to kill him until we have found where he has hidden them.' So they changed back to the shapes of dog and stick and went to sleep.

The next morning the woman and her boy set off to the forest near the mountain to gather berries and to dig up medicine roots. They took the dog and the stick with them. At noon, after they had worked for some time, they sat down to have their luncheon. The woman threw the stick down on the ground and the boy let the dog run away among the shrubs.

The dog wandered to the side of the mountain. There he found an opening like the mouth of a cave. Peering into the place, he saw many buffaloes within, and he knew that at last he had found the hiding-place of the giant's plunder. He went back to the woman and the boy and began to bark. This was the signal agreed on with his companion. The woman and her son thought he was barking at a bird, and they laughed at his capers as he jumped about. But he was in reality calling to his comrade. The stick understood the call and wiggled like a snake through the underbrush to the dog's side, unseen by the boy and his mother. They then entered the large cave in the side of the mountain, and there they found a great herd of buffaloes—all the buffaloes that had been driven from the prairies. The dog barked at them and snapped at their heels and the stick beat them, and they began to drive them quickly out of the cavern and eastward toward the plains. But they still kept the shape of dog and stick.

When evening came and it was time for the boy and his mother to go home, the boy searched for the dog and the woman looked for her stick, but they could not find them, and they had to go home without them.

Just as the woman and her son reached their house on the bank of the river, the giant-thief was coming home too. He chanced to look to the east, and there he saw, far away, many buffaloes running towards the foot-hills where the sweet-grass grew. He was very angry, and he cried loudly to his son: 'Where is the dog? Where is the dog?'

'I lost him in the underbrush,' said the boy; 'he chased a bird and did not come back.'

'It was not a bird he chased,' said the giant; 'it was one of my buffaloes. I told you he was an evil thing and not to touch him, but you and your mother would have your way. Now my buffaloes are all gone.' He gnashed his teeth in a great rage and rushed off to the hidden cave to see if any buffaloes were left, crying as he went: 'I will kill the dog if I find him.'

When he reached the cave the Chief and the youth, still in the form of a dog and a stick, were just rounding up the last of the buffaloes. The giant rushed at them to kill the dog and to break the stick, but they sprang upon an old buffalo and hid in his long hair and, clinging on tightly, the dog bit the buffalo until the old animal plunged and roared and rushed from the cave, bearing the Chief and the youth concealed on his back. He galloped eastward until he reached the herd far away on the prairie, leaving the giant far behind to make the best of his anger. Then the Chief and the brave youth took their old form of men, and in high spirits they drove the herd of buffaloes back to their hungry people waiting patiently on the plains.

The people were very pleased to see the Great Chief and the youth returning to the village with the great herd of fat buffaloes, for they knew now that the famine was ended. But as they drove the animals into a great fenced enclosure, a large grey bird flew over their heads and swooped down upon them and pecked at them with its bill, and tried to frighten them and drive them away. The Great Chief knew by his magic power that the grey bird was none other than the giant-thief who had stolen the buffaloes, and who had changed himself into a bird to fly across the prairies in pursuit of them. Then the Chief changed himself into an otter and lay down on the bank of the stream pretending to be dead. The grey bird flew down upon him, for he thought he would have a good meal of fat otter. But the Chief seized him by the leg and, changing back to his own form, he bore him in triumph to his camp. He tied him up fast to the smoke-hole of his tent and made a great fire inside. The giant cried: 'Spare me, spare me, and I shall never do you more harm!' But the Chief left him on the tent pole all night long while the black smoke from the fire poured out around him. In the morning his feathers were all black. Then the Chief let him down, and he said: 'You may go now, but you will never be able to resume your former shape. You will henceforth be a raven, a bird of ill-omen upon the earth, an outlaw and a brigand among the birds, despised among men because of your thefts. And you will always have to steal and to hunt hard for your food.'

And to this day the feathers of the raven are black, and he is a bird of ill-omen upon the earth because of his encounter with the Great Chieftain long ago.

The Boy of the Red Twilight Sky

Long ago there dwelt on the shores of the Great Water
in the west a young man and his younger wife. They had
no children and they lived all by themselves far from
other people on an island not far from the coast. The
man spent his time in catching the deep-sea fish far out
on the ocean, or in spearing salmon in the distant rivers.
Often he was gone for many days and his wife was very
lonely in his absence. She was not afraid, for she had a
stout spirit, but it was very dismal in the evenings to look
only at the grey leaden sky and to hear only the sound
of the surf as it beat upon the beach. So day after day she
said to herself: 'I wish we had children. They would be
good company for me when I am alone and my husband
is far away.'

One evening at twilight, when she was solitary because of her husband's absence on the ocean catching the deep-sea fish, she sat on the sand beach looking out across the water. The sky in the west was pale grey; it was always dull and grey in that country, and when the sun had gone down there was no soft light. In her loneliness the woman said to herself: 'I wish we had children to keep me company.'

A Kingfisher, with his children, was diving for minnows not far away. And the woman said: 'Oh, sea-bird with the white collar! I wish we had children like you.' And the Kingfisher said: 'Look in the sea-shells, look in the sea-shells,' and flew away.

The next evening the woman sat again upon the beach looking westward at the dull grey sky. Not far away a white Sea-gull was riding on the waves in the midst of her brood of little ones. And the woman said: 'Oh, white sea-bird! I wish we had children like you to keep us company.' And the Sea-gull said: 'Look in the sea-shells, look in the sea-shells,' and flew away.

The woman wondered greatly at the words of the Kingfisher and the Sea-gull. As she sat there in thought she heard a strange cry coming from the sand dunes behind her. She went closer to the sound and found that the cry came from a large sea-shell lying on the sand. She picked up the shell, and inside of it was a tiny boy crying as hard as he could. She was well pleased with her discovery, and she carried the baby to her home and cared for him. When her husband came home from the sea, he, too, was very happy to find the baby there, for he knew that they would be lonely no more.

The baby grew very rapidly, and soon he was able to

walk and move about where he pleased. One day the woman was wearing a copper bracelet on her arm, and the child said to her: 'I must have a bow made from the copper on your arm.' So to please him she made him a tiny bow from the bracelet, and two tiny arrows. At once he set out to hunt game, and day after day he came home bearing the products of his chase. He brought home geese and ducks and brant and small sea-birds, and gave them to his mother for food. As he grew older the man and his wife noticed that his face took on a golden hue brighter than the colour of his copper bow. Wherever he went there was a strange light. When he sat on the beach looking to the west, the weather was always calm and there were strange bright gleams upon the water. And his foster-parents wondered greatly at this unusual power. But the boy would not talk about it; when they spoke of it he was always silent.

It happened once that the winds blew hard over the Great Water and the man could not go to catch fish because of the turbulent sea. For many days he stayed on shore, for the ocean, which was usually at peace, was lashed into a great fury and the waves were dashing high on the beach. Soon the people were in need of fish for food. And the boy said: 'I will go out with you, for I can overcome the Storm Spirit.' The man did not want to go, but at last he listened to the boy's entreaties, and together they set out for the fishing grounds far across the tossing sea.

They had not gone far when they met the Spirit of the Storm coming madly from the south-west where the great winds dwelt. He tried hard to upset their boat, but over them he had no power, for the boy guided the frail craft across the water and all around them the sea was calm and still. Then the Storm Spirit called his nephew Black Cloud to help him, and away in the south-east they saw him hurrying to his uncle's aid. But the boy said to the man: 'Be not afraid, for I am more than a match for him.' So the two met, but when Black Cloud saw the boy he quickly disappeared. Then the Spirit of the Storm called Mist of the Sea to come and cover the water, for he thought the boat would be lost if he hid the land from the man and the boy. When the man saw Mist of the Sea coming like a grey vapour across the water he was very frightened, for of all his enemies on the ocean he feared this one most. But the boy said: 'He cannot harm you when I am with you.' And sure enough, when Mist of the Sea saw the boy sitting smiling in the boat, he disappeared as quickly as he had come. And the Storm Spirit in great anger hurried away to other parts, and that day there was no more danger on the sea near the fishing grounds.

The boy and the man soon reached the fishing grounds in safety. And the boy taught his foster-father a magic song with which he was able to lure fish to his nets. Before evening came, the boat was filled with good fat fish and they set out for their home. The man said: 'Tell me the secret of your power.' But the boy said: 'It is not yet time.'

The next day the boy killed many birds. He skinned them all and dried their skins. Then he dressed himself in the skin of a plover and rose into the air and flew above the sea. And the sea under him was grey like his wings. Then he came down and dressed himself in the skin of a blue-jay and soared away again. And the sea over which he was flying was at once changed to blue like the blue of his wings. When he came back to the beach, he put on the skin of a robin with the breast of a golden hue like his face. Then he flew high and at once the waves under him reflected a colour as of fire, and bright gleams of light appeared upon the ocean, and the sky in the west was golden red.

The boy flew back to the beach and he said to his foster-parents: 'Now it is time for me to leave you. I am the offspring of the sun. Yesterday my power was tested and it was not found wanting, so now I must go away and I shall see you no more. But at evening I shall appear to you often in the twilight sky in the west. And when the sky and the sea look at evening like the colour of my face, you will know that there will be no wind nor storm and that on the morrow the weather will be fair. But although I go away, I shall leave you a strange power. And always when you need me, let me know your desires by making white offerings to me, so that I may see them from my home far in the west.'

Then he gave to his foster-mother a wonderful robe. He bade his parents goodbye and soared away to the west, leaving them in sadness. But the woman still keeps a part of the power he gave her, and when she sits on the island in a crevice in the dunes and loosens her wonderful robe, the wind hurries down from the land, and the sea is ruffled with storm; and the more she loosens the garment the greater is the tempest. But in the late autumn, when the cold mists come in from the sea and the evenings are chill and the sky is dull and grey, she remembers the promise of the boy. And she makes to him an offering of tiny white feathers plucked from the breasts

of birds. She throws them into the air, and they appear as flakes of snow and rise thickly into the winds. And they hurry westward to tell the boy that the world is grey and dreary as it yearns for the sight of his golden face. Then he appears to the people of earth. He comes at evening and lingers after the sun has gone, until the twilight sky is red and the ocean in the west has gleams of golden light. And the people then know that there will be no wind and that on the morrow the weather will be fair, as he promised them long ago.

The Girl Who Always Cried

On the bank of a stream far in the west, Owl-man lived long ago in a little house under the ground. He had very strange habits. He always kept away from the Great Water and he dwelt for the most part in the forest. He had very few friends, and he usually went hunting by himself. He lived on toads and frogs and flies. He would say but little, and when other people sat around him talking pleasantly, he was always silent, gazing into space with wide-open eyes and trying to look wiser than he really was. Because of this, people thought he was very queer, and strange stories about him soon spread far and wide. It was said that he was very cruel, and that he was silent because he was always brooding over his past wickedness or thinking about some evil deed he was soon going to do. And when children were troublesome or disobedient, their mothers always frightened them into goodness by saying: 'The Owl-man from the stream will come and take you if you do not mend your ways.' And although

the Owl-man was a solitary fellow, he thus had great in-
fluence in all the land.

Not far away lived a man and a woman who had one
adopted daughter. Because she was the only child in the
house she was much petted, and she was never satisfied,
and she cried and fretted all the time, and kept always
asking for things she could not get. She disturbed all the
neighbours round about so that they could not sleep because of her constant wailing and complaining. At last
her foster-parents grew tired of her weeping and they
said: 'The Owl-man will carry you off if you do not stop
crying.' But still she pouted and fretted. And the old
man of the house said: 'I wish the Owl-man would come
and take her away.'

Now the old man was a great magician, and as he
wished, so it came to pass. That evening it happened that
the people were gathered at a feast of shell-fish on the
beach by the bright moonlight, as was their weekly custom. But the sorrowful girl would not go with the others.
She stayed at home and sulked. As she sat alone in the
house, the old Owl-man came along carrying his basket
full of toads and frogs. The girl was still crying when he
came in. 'I have come for you,' he said, 'as the old man
wished.' And he put her in his basket with the toads and
frogs and carried her off. She yelled and kicked and
scratched, but the lid of the basket was tightly closed and
Owl-man laughed to himself and said: 'Now I have a wife
at last. I shall be alone no more, and the people will not
now think I am so queer.' So he took her to his under-
ground house by the stream.

That night the people noticed that the girl's cries were
no longer heard, and they said: 'What can have cured

Sour-face? What can have pleased Cry-baby into silence?'
And the girl's foster-mother wondered where she had
gone. But only the old man knew that it had happened
as he had wished, because of his magic power, and that
Owl-man had taken her away.

The girl was not happy in her new home, for she would
not be happy in any place. She still kept up her cater-
wauling and there was no peace in the house. Owl-man
was a great hunter. Every day he went out hunting with
his big basket on his arm, but he always locked his wife
in the house before he went away. He was always very
successful in the chase, and each night he came back with
his basket full of toads and frogs and field-mice and flies.
But his wife would eat none of them and she threw them
in his face when he offered them to her, and said in a bad
temper: 'I will not eat your filthy food. It is not fit food
for gentlefolk.' And Owl-man said: 'Gentlefolk indeed!
You should find a more suitable name. You are not gentle;
you are a wild evil thing, but I am going to tame you.'
And the girl wept again and sulked and stamped her feet
in her temper.

At last the girl became very hungry, for there was little
to eat except the food that Owl-man brought home for
himself. He gathered a few berries for her, but even these
did not satisfy her hunger. So she thought out a plan of
escape. One day when Owl-man was away, she took some
oil she found in the house and rubbed it all over her face
and hair. When Owl-man came home in the evening, he
said: 'You are very pretty tonight. What have you done to
make yourself look so sleek and shiny?' And she answered:
'I have put on my face and hair gum which I picked from
the trees last night when I went walking with you.' And

he said: 'I should like to put some on too, for perhaps it would make me beautiful.' The girl told him that if he would go out and gather some gum she would put it on his face and hair for him. So he went out and gathered a great store of gum from the trees and brought it back to her. She melted it on a hot stove until it was balsam again and would pour easily out. Then she said: 'Shut your eyes so that it will not harm your sight and I will make your face and hair beautiful and shining like mine.' Owl-man shut his eyes, and the girl soon covered his face and head with the soft gum. She put it on very thick, and she said: 'Keep your eyes shut until it dries or it may blind you.' Owl-man did as he was told, but when the gum dried he could not open his eyes, and while he was trying to rub it off, the girl slipped out the door and ran back to her parents, far away by the Great Water.

Owl-man scraped the gum from his face and head as best he could, and when he could open his eyes again and could see pretty well, he went out into the night in search of his wife. And as he went along he cried: 'Oh, oh, oh! Where is my wife? Where is my girl? I have lost my wife. I have lost my girl. Oh, oh, oh!' And when the people heard him calling they thought they would play a trick on him. So they said: 'She is here, she is here.' But when he entered their houses, the woman they showed him was not his wife, and he went away sorrowful. And the people all laughed at his confusion and said: 'Owl-man is getting queerer each day. He is far gone in his head.'

Owl-man went from house to house, but he could not find his wife. Then he went to the trees and searched among the branches. He pulled the trees up by the roots, thinking she might be hiding underneath. And he looked

into the salmon-traps in the rivers, and kicked them to pieces in his frenzy. But nowhere was his wife to be found.

Then he went to the girl's house, where she was hiding, and he yelled: 'Oh, oh, oh! Give me my wife! Give me my girl! I know she is here. Oh, oh, oh!' But the girl's foster-mother would not give her up. Then he began to tear down the house over their heads, for the old man of the house was away and there was no one else strong enough to stop Owl-man in his rage. When the woman saw her house in danger of falling about her ears, she cried: 'Stop! Your wife is here.' And she brought forth the girl from her hiding-place. When Owl-man saw her, his rage left him and he was happy again.

But just then the old man of magic power came home. He had heard the hubbub from a distance. When he came in and saw the great holes in the roof and the side of his house where Owl-man had torn away the logs, he was very angry and he said to himself: 'I will punish both Owl-man and the girl for this night's work.' And he hit upon a plan. He said to Owl-man: 'We must give you a hot bath to melt the gum and take it from your hair, for it will do you no good and it will take all the hair off your head.' And Owl-man gladly agreed. So they filled a great bark tub with water and heated it by placing at the bottom of it many red-hot stones, after the fashion of Indians in those old days. But the old man put so many hot stones in the water that it was soon almost boiling with the heat, and when they put Owl-man into the tub he was almost scalded to death and he yelled loudly in pain.

Then the old man said: 'Now I will take vengeance. You will trouble me no more. You have broken my house. Henceforth you will be not a man but an Owl, and you will dwell alone in the forest with few friends, and you will live always on frogs and toads and field-mice, and people will hear you at night crying for your wife all over the land, but you shall never find her.' Then with his magic power he changed him to an Owl and sent him on his way.

He said to the girl: 'You have done me much harm too, and you have brought all this trouble upon me. Henceforth you will be not a girl but a Fish-Hawk, and you will always cry and fret and scream as you have done before, and you will never be satisfied.' And with his magic power he changed her into a Fish-Hawk and sent her out to the ocean. And there she screams always, and she is a great glutton, for she can never get enough to eat. And since that time, Owl and Fish-Hawk have not dwelt together and have not been on friendly terms. They live far apart, and Owl keeps to the forest and the mountains, while the other keeps to the sea. Thus was the old man avenged, and thus was the weeping maiden punished for her tears. And the cries of Owl and Fish-Hawk are still heard in many places, one calling for his wife, the other screaming unsatisfied for something she cannot get.

How Raven Brought Fire to the Indians

Many ages ago when the world was still young, Raven
and White Sea-gull lived near together in Canada, far
in the north country on the shores of the Great Water in
the west. They were very good friends and they always
worked in harmony and they had much food and many
servants in common. White Sea-gull knew no guile: he
was always very open and frank and honest in his deal-
ings with others. But Raven was a sly fellow, and at times
he was not lacking in treachery and deceit. But Sea-gull
did not suspect him, and the two lived always on very
friendly terms.

In these far-back times in the north country, all the
world was dark and there was no light but that of the
stars. Sea-gull owned all the daylight, but he was very
stingy and he kept it always locked up in a box. He would
give none of it to anyone else, and he never let it out of

the box except when he needed a little of it to help himself when he went far away on his journeys.

After a time Raven grew envious of Sea-gull's posses-
sion, and he said: 'It is not fair that Sea-gull should keep
the daylight all to himself locked up in a box. It was
meant for all the world and not for him alone, and it
would be of great value to all of us if he would sometimes
let a little of it out.' So he went to Sea-gull and said: 'Give
me some of your daylight. You do not need it all and I
can use some of it with advantage.' But Sea-gull said:
'No. I want it all for myself. What could you do with
daylight, you with your coat as black as night?' and he
would not give him any of it. So Raven made up his mind
that he would have to get some daylight from Sea-gull by
stealth.

Soon afterwards Raven gathered some prickly thorns
and burdocks and scattered them on the ground between
Sea-gull's house and the beach where the canoes were lying. Then he went to Sea-gull's window and cried loudly:
'Our canoes are going adrift in the surf. Come quickly
and help me to save them.' Sea-gull sprang out of bed and
ran half-asleep on his bare feet. But as he ran to the
beach the thorns stuck in his bare flesh and he howled
with pain. He crawled back to his house, saying: 'My
canoe may go adrift if it pleases. I cannot walk because
of the splinters in my feet.' Raven chuckled to himself
and he moved away, pretending to go to the beach to
draw up the canoes.

Then he went into Sea-gull's house. Sea-gull was still
howling with pain; he was sitting crying on the side of
his bed and he was trying to pull the thorns from his feet
as best he could. 'I will help you,' said Raven, 'for I have

often done this before. I am a very good doctor.' So he took
an awl made from whale-bone and he caught hold of Sea-
gull's foot with the pretence of removing the thorns. But
instead of taking them out he only pushed them in farther until poor Sea-gull howled louder than ever. And
Raven said: 'It is so dark I cannot see to pull these thorns
from your feet. Give me some daylight and I will soon
cure you. A doctor must always have a little light.' So Sea-
gull unlocked the box and lifted the cover just a little
bit so that a faint gleam of light came out. 'That is better,' said Raven. But instead of picking out the thorns he
pushed them in as he had done before, until Sea-gull
howled and kicked in pain. 'Why are you so stingy with
your light?' snapped Raven. 'Do you think I am an owl
and that I can see well enough in the darkness to heal
your feet? Open the box wide and I will soon make you
well.' So saying, he purposely fell heavily against Sea-gull
and knocked the box on the floor. The cover flew open
and daylight escaped and spread quickly over all the
world.

Poor Sea-gull tried his best to lure it back again into
the box, but his efforts proved fruitless, for it had gone
forever. Raven said he was very sorry for the accident,
but after he had taken all the thorns from Sea-gull's feet,
he went home laughing to himself and well pleased because of the success of his trick.

Soon there was light in all the world. But Raven could
not see very well, for the light was too bright and his
eyes were not accustomed to it. He sat for a time looking
towards the east, but he saw there nothing of interest.
The next day he saw a bit farther, for he was now getting
used to the new conditions. The third day he could see

distinctly a line of hills far in the east, rising against the sky and covered with a blue mist. He looked long at the strange sight. Then he saw far away towards the hill a thin column of smoke lifting heavenwards. He had never seen smoke before, but he had often heard of it from travellers in strange places. 'That must be the country of which I have been told,' he said. 'In that land dwell the people who alone possess Fire. We have searched for it for many ages and now I think we have found it.' Then he thought: 'We now have the daylight, and what a fine thing it would be if we could also have Fire!' And he determined to set out to find it.

On the following day he called his servants together and told them of his plans. He said: 'We shall set out at once, for the distance is far.' And he asked three of his best servants, Robin, Mole, and Flea, to go with him. Flea brought out his little wagon and they all tried to get into it, but it was much too small to hold them. Then they tried Mole's carriage, but it was much too frail and it had scarcely started to move when it broke down and they all fell out in a heap. Then they tried Robin's carriage, but it was much too high and it toppled over under its heavy load and threw them all to the ground. Then Raven stole Sea-gull's large strong carriage (for Sea-gull was asleep) and it did very well, and they started on their journey, taking turns pushing the carriage along with a pole over the flat plain.

After a strange journey in queer places they reached the land of the people who owned Fire, guided along by the thin column of smoke. The people were not people of earth. Some say they were the Fish people, but that no man knows. They sat around in a large circle with Fire in their midst, for it was autumn and the days and nights were chill. And Fire was in many places.

Raven looked on for a while from afar, thinking of the best plan to obtain Fire. Then he said to Robin: 'You can move faster than any of us. You must steal Fire. You can fly in quickly, pick it up in your bill and take it back to us, and the people will not see nor hear you.' So Robin picked out a spot where there were few people, and he darted in quickly and picked up Fire in a twinkling and flew back unharmed towards his companions. But he had only taken a very little bit of it. When he got half-way back to his friends, Fire was so hot in his bill that it gave him a strange pain and he had to drop it on the ground. It fell to the earth with a crash and it was so small that it flickered faintly. Robin called to his companions to bring the carriage. Then he stood over Fire and fanned it with his wings to keep it alive. It was very hot, but he stood bravely to his task until his breast was badly scorched and he had to move away. His efforts to save Fire were of no avail, and before his companions reached him Fire had died, and only a black coal remained. And poor Robin's breast was singed, and to this day the breasts of his descendants are a reddish-brown colour because he was scorched while trying to steal Fire ages ago.

Then Raven asked Flea to make the attempt to steal Fire. But Flea said: 'I am too little. The heat would roast me to death; and, further, I might miscalculate the distance and hop into the flame.' Then Raven asked Mole to try, but Mole said: 'Oh, no. I am better fitted for other work. My fur would all be singed like Robin's breast.'

Raven took good care that he would not go himself, for he was a great coward. So he said: 'There is a better and easier way. We will steal the baby of the Chief and hold him for ransom. Perhaps they will give us Fire in exchange for him,' and they all thought this was a very good idea. Raven asked: 'Who will volunteer to steal the baby?' for he always made the others do all the work. Flea said: 'I will go. In one jump I will be into the house, and in another jump I will be out again, for I can hop a great distance.' But the others laughed and said: 'You could not carry the baby. You are too small.' The Mole said: 'I will go. I can tunnel a passage very quietly under the house and right up to the baby's cradle. I can then steal the baby and no one will hear me or see me.' So it was agreed that Mole should go. In a few minutes Mole made his tunnel, and he was soon back with the baby. Then they got into their carriage and hurried home with their prize.

When the Chief of the Fire People discovered the loss of his child he was very angry. And in all the land there was great sorrow because the Chief's heir, the hope of the tribe, had gone. And the child's mother and her women wept so bitterly that their tears fell like rain on all the land. The Chief said he would give anything he possessed to find his child. But although his people searched far and near, they could not find the baby.

After many days a wayfarer who had come far from the Great Water in the west brought them news that a strange child was living far to the westward in the village by the sea. He said: 'He is not of their tribe; he looks like the children of your village,' and he advised them to go to see him for themselves. So the Chief sent his men to search for them, guided by the wayfarer. When they reached Raven's village they were told that a strange baby was indeed there; the child was described to them, but he was kept out of sight, and Raven would not tell how he had happened to come there. And Raven said: 'How do I know he is your Chief's child? People tell strange lies these days. If you want him you can pay for him, for he has caused us much trouble and expense.' So the messengers went back and reported to the Chief what they had heard. From the description the Chief knew that the child was his, so he gave the messengers very valuable presents of pearls and rich robes and sent them back again to ransom his boy. But Raven, when he saw the presents, said: 'No, I do not want these gifts; they do not pay me for my trouble,' and he would not part with the baby. The messengers again reported to the Chief what had happened. Then the Chief gave them still richer gifts, the best he had in all his land, and sent them back. But again Raven said: 'No, your gifts are valueless compared with my trouble and expense. Say this to your Chief.'

When the Chief heard this from his messengers he was sore perplexed, for he had offered the best he had, and he thought that he had reached the end of his resources. So he said: 'Go back and ask the people to demand what they wish in exchange for my boy and they will receive it if it can be provided.' So the messengers went back to Raven and spoke as they had been commanded. And Raven said: 'Only one thing can pay for the child, and that is Fire. Give me Fire and you can take the baby.' The messenger laughed and said: 'Why did you not say so at first and save us all this trouble and anxiety? Fire is the most plentiful thing in our kingdom, and we hold it in no value.' So they returned happy to the Chief. And he sent back much Fire and received his child unharmed from

Raven in exchange. And he sent Raven two small stones which the messengers taught Raven how to use. And they said: 'If you ever lose Fire or if it dies for lack of food, you can always call it back to life with these two little stones.' Then they showed him how to make Fire with the two little stones and withered grass and birch-bark and dry pine, and Raven thought it was very easy. And he felt very proud because he had brought Fire and Light to the earth.

He kept Fire for himself for a long time and, although the people clamoured loudly for it, he would not give any of it away. Soon, however, he decided to sell a quantity of it, for he now had the power of making it. So he said to himself: 'This is a good way to get many wives,' and he announced that he would only sell some of his Fire in return for a wife. And many families bought his Fire and in exchange he received many wives. And to this day he still has many wives and he still moves about from place to place with a flock of them always around him. But the Indians, when they arrived, took Fire away from him. Thus Fire came to the Indians in the olden days. And when it has died, as it often does, they still sometimes use Raven's flint stones to bring it back to life.

The Youth and the Dog Dance

Once long ago, when the Indians dwelt in the country in the northwest, a youth went far away from his native village to catch birds. His people lived near a lake where only small birds nested, and as he wanted large and bright-coloured feathers for his arrows and his bonnet, he had to go far into the forest, where larger birds of brilliant plumage lived. When he reached the Land of Many Feathers far in the north country, he dug a pit on the top of a high hill. Then he covered the pit with poles and over the poles he spread grass and leaves so that the place looked like the earth around it. He put meat and corn on the grass, and tied the food to the poles so that the birds could not carry it away. Then he climbed down into the pit and waited for the birds to come, when he could reach up and catch them by the feet and kill them.

All day long and far into the night the youth waited for birds, but no birds came. Towards morning he heard a distant sound like that of a partridge drumming. But the sound did not come nearer. The next night, as the youth watched and waited in the pit, he heard the same sound, and he said: 'I will see where the noise comes from and I will discover the cause, for it is not a partridge, and it is very strange.' So he climbed out of the pit and went in the direction of the sound. He walked along rapidly through the forest until he came at dawn to the shore of a large lake. The drumming came from somewhere in the lake, but as he stood listening to it, the sound suddenly stopped.

The next night the youth heard the drumming louder than before. Again he went to the lake. The sound was again distinct as it rose from the water, and when he looked he saw great numbers of birds and animals swimming in the lake in the moonlight. But there was no explanation of the strange sound. As he sat watching the animals and birds, he prayed to his guardian spirit to tell him the cause of the drumming. Soon an old man came along. He was old and bent and wrinkled, but his eyes were kind. The youth gave him some tobacco and they sat down together on the edge of the lake and watched the swimmers in the dim light and smoked their pipes.

'What are you doing here?' asked the old man.

'I am trying to learn the cause of the strange drumming,' said the youth.

'You do well indeed to seek it,' said the old man, 'and to seek to know the cause of all things. Only in that way will you be great and wise. But remember, there are some things the cause of which you can never find.'

'Where have you come from?' said the boy.

'Oh,' said the man, 'I lived once upon a time like you in the Country of Fancy where great dreams dwell, and indeed I live there still, but your dreams are all of the future while mine are of the past. But some day you too will change and your thoughts will be like mine.'

'Tell me the cause of the drumming,' said the boy.

And the old man said: 'Take this wand that I will give you and wave it before you go to sleep, and maybe you will see strange things.' Then he gave the boy a wand and disappeared into the forest, and the boy never saw him again.

The boy waved the wand and fell asleep on the sand as the old man had told him. When he awoke he found himself in a large room in the midst of many people. Some of them were dancing gracefully, and some sat around and talked. They wore wonderful robes of skins and feathers of many different colours. The boy wished he could get such feathers for his own clothes and his bonnet. But as he looked at the people he was suddenly aware that they were none other than the animals and birds he had seen for two nights swimming in the lake in the moonlight. They were now changed into human form through some strange and miraculous power. They were very kind to the youth and treated him with great courtesy.

At last the dancing ceased and the talking stopped, and one who seemed to be the Chief stood up at the end of the room and said: 'Oh, young stranger, the Great Spirit has heard your prayers, and because of your magic wand we have been sent to you in these shapes. The creatures you see here are the animals and birds of the world. I am the Dog, whom the Great Spirit loves well. I have much power, and my power I shall give to you, and I shall always protect you and guard you. And even if you should treat me with cruelty I shall never be unfaithful to you,

nor shall I ever be unkind. But you must take this Dance home with you and teach it to your people and they must celebrate the Dance once a year.' Then he taught the youth the secrets of their Dance.

When the youth had learned the Dance, the Chief turned to his companions and said: 'My comrades and brothers, I have taught the young stranger the secrets of the Dance. I have given him my own power. Will you not have pity on a creature from earth and give him some of the power of which you too are possessed?'

For a long time no one spoke, but at last Owl arose and said: 'I too will help him. I have power to see far in the darkness and to hunt by night. When he goes out at night I will be near him and he shall see a great distance. I give him these feathers to fasten in his hair.' And the Owl gave him a bunch of feathers which the youth tied to his head.

Then Buffalo came forward and said: 'I too will help him. I will give him my endurance and my strength, and my power to trample my enemies underfoot. And I give him this belt of tanned buffalo-hide to wear when he goes to war.' And he gave the youth a very wondrous belt to fasten around his waist.

The animals and birds, one after the other, gave him gladly of their power. Porcupine gave him quills with which to decorate his leather belt and his bonnet, and he said: 'I too will aid you, and when you make war I will be near you. I can make my enemies as weak as children, and they always flee when I approach, for they fear the shooting of my quills. When you meet your foes you will always overcome them, for I give you power as it was given to me.'

And Bear said: 'I will give you my toughness and my strength, and a strip of fur for your leather belt and your coat. And when you are in danger, I will not be far away.'

Then Deer said: 'I give you my swiftness so that you may be fleet of foot. And when you pursue your enemies you will always overtake them, and should you flee from them, you will always out-run them in the race.'

Then the birds spoke again, and Crane said: 'I give you a bone from my wings to make a war-whistle to frighten your enemies away or to summon your people to your assistance when you need them. And I give you my wings for your head-dress.'

The giant Eagle then spoke and said: 'Oh, youth, I will be with you wherever you go, and I will give you my strength and my power in war. And even as I do, you will always see your enemies from afar, and you can always escape them if you so desire.' And he gave him a large bunch of wonderful eagle feathers to tie in his hair as a token of his fidelity.

And finally, Wild-Cat said: 'I give you my power to crawl stealthily through the grass and the underbrush and to spring unexpectedly on your foes and take them unawares. And I give you too my power of hiding from my enemies.' And he gave him strips of his fur to decorate his clothing in token of his friendship.

From all the animals and the birds the youth received power and gifts. Then he waved his magic wand and lay down to sleep. When he awoke, he found himself on the shore of the lake, and far in the east the dawn was breaking. But he could see farther than he had ever seen before, and away in the distance he could make out blue hills and smoke rising from far-off villages. And he knew that strange power was upon him. But not a sound came from the lake, and the drumming had forever ended.

The youth took his magic wand and his gifts and set out for his home. And he told his people what had happened and he taught them the secrets of the Dance which was to make them strong and victorious in war. And among his people it became a great ceremony and was practised for long ages, and was known as the Dog Dance. And since that time, the animals and birds have been friends to the Indians, and the Indians have acquired much of their cunning and skill and power. And ever after the night of moonlight by the lake when the youth with the magic wand received the strange gifts, the Indians have decorated their war clothes with fur and quills and feathers from the animals and the birds. And in the far north country the Dog Dance is still held at intervals out of gratitude for the gifts, for the Indians do not forget the promise of long ago.

The Boy in the Land of Shadows

Two orphan children, a boy and a girl, lived alone near the mountains. Their parents had long been dead and the children were left to look after themselves without any kindred upon the earth. The boy hunted all day long and provided much food, and the girl kept the house in order and did the cooking. They had a very deep love for each other and as they grew up they said: 'We shall never leave each other. We shall always stay here together.' But one year it happened that in the early springtime it was very cold. The snow lingered on the plains and the ice moved slowly from the rivers and chill winds were always blowing and grey vapours hovered over all the land. And there was very little food to be had, for the animals hid in their warm winter dens and the wild-geese and ducks were still far south. And in this cruel period of bad weather the little girl sickened and died. Her brother worked hard to provide her with nourishing food and he gathered all the medicine roots he thought could bring her relief, but it was all to no purpose. And despite all his efforts, one evening in the twilight his sister went away to the west, leaving him alone behind upon the earth.

The boy was heart-broken because of his sister's death. And when the late spring came and the days grew warm and food was plentiful again, he said: 'She must be somewhere in the west, for they say that our people do not really die. I will go and search for her, and perhaps I can find her and bring her back.' So one morning he set out on his strange quest. He journeyed many days westward towards the Great Water, killing game for food as he went and sleeping at night under the stars. He met many strange people, but he did not tell them the purpose of his travels. At last he came to the shore of the Great Water, and he sat looking towards the sunset wondering what next to do. In the evening an old man came along. 'What are you doing here?' asked the man. 'I am looking for my sister,' said the boy. 'Some time ago she sickened and died and I am lonely without her and I want to find her and bring her back.' And the man said: 'Some time ago she whom you seek passed this way. If you wish to find her you must undertake a dangerous journey.' The boy answered that he would gladly risk any dangers to find his sister, and the old man said: 'I will help you. Your sister has gone to the Land of Shadows far away in the Country of Silence which lies out yonder in the Island of the Blest. To reach the Island you must sail far into the west, but I warn you that it is a perilous journey, for the crossing is always rough and your boat will be tossed by tempests. But you will be well repaid for your trouble, for in that land nobody is ever hungry or tired; there is no death and no sorrow; there are no tears, and no one ever grows old.'

Then the old man gave the boy a large pipe and some tobacco and said: 'This will help you in your need.' And he brought him to where a small canoe lay dry upon the beach. It was a wonderful canoe, the most beautiful the boy had ever seen. It was cut from a single white stone and it sparkled in the red twilight like a polished jewel. And the old man said: 'This canoe will weather all storms. But see that you handle it carefully, and when you come back, see that you leave it in the cove where you found it.'

Soon afterwards the boy set out on his journey. The moon was full and the night was cold with stars. He sailed into the west over a rough and angry sea, but he was in no danger, for his canoe rode easily on the waters. All around him he saw in the moonlight many other canoes going in the same direction and all white and shining like his own. But no one seemed to be guiding them, and although he looked long at them, not a person could he make out. He wondered if the canoes were drifting un-occupied, for when he called to them there was no an-swer. Sometimes a canoe upset in the tossing sea and the waves rose over it and it was seen no more, and the boy often thought he heard an anguished cry. For several days he sailed on to the west, and all the time other canoes were not far away and all the time some of them were dropping from sight beneath the surging waters, but he saw no people in them.

At last, after a long journey, the sea grew calm and the air was sweet and warm. There was no trace of the storm, for the waves were quiet and the sky was as clear as crystal. He saw that he was near the Island of the Blest of which the old man had spoken, for it was now plain to his view as it rose above the ocean, topped with green grass and trees and a snow-white beach. Soon he reached the shore and drew up his canoe. As he turned away he came upon a skeleton lying flat upon the sand. He stopped to look at it, and as he did so the skeleton sat up and said in great surprise: 'You should not be here. Why have you come?' and the boy said: 'I seek my sister. In the early springtime she sickened and died, and I am going to the Land of Shadows in the Country of Silence in search of her.' 'You must go far inland,' said the skeleton, 'and the way is hard to find for such as you.' The boy asked for guidance, and the skeleton said: 'Let me smoke and I will help you.' The boy gave him the pipe and the tobacco he had received from the old man, and he laughed when he saw his strange companion with the pipe between his teeth. The skeleton smoked for some time and at last, as the smoke rose from his pipe, it changed to a flock of little white birds which flew about like doves. The boy looked on in wonder, and the skeleton said: 'These birds will guide you. Follow them.' Then he gave back the pipe and stretched out again flat upon the sand, and the boy could not rouse him from his sleep.

The boy followed the little white birds as he had been told. He went along through a land of great beauty where flowers were blooming and countless birds were singing. Not a person did he meet on the way. The place was deserted except for the song-birds and the flowers. He passed through the Country of Silence, and came to a mysterious land where no one dwelt. But although he saw no one, he heard many voices and he could not tell whence they came. They seemed to be all around him. At last the birds stopped at the entrance to a great garden and flew around his head in a circle. They would go no further and they alighted on a tree close by, all except one, which perched on the boy's shoulder. The lad knew that here at last was the Land of Shadows.

When he entered the garden he heard again many low voices. But he saw no one. He saw only many shadows of people on the grass, but he could not see from what the shadows came. He wondered greatly at the strange and unusual sight, for back in his homeland in that time the sunlight made no shadows. He listened again to the voices and he knew now that the shadows were speaking. He wandered about for some time marvelling greatly at the strange place with its weird unearthly beauty. At last he heard a voice which he knew to be his sister's. It was soft and sweet, just as he had known it when they were together on the earth, and it had not changed since she left him. He went to the shadow from which the voice came and, throwing himself on the grass beside it, he said: 'I have long sought you, my sister. I have come to take you home. Let me see you as you were when we dwelt together.' But his sister said: 'You have done wisely to keep me in your memory and to seek to find me. But here we cannot appear to the people of earth except as shadows. I cannot go back with you, for it is now too late. I have eaten of the food of this land; if you had come before I had eaten, perhaps you could have taken me away. Who knows? But my heart and voice are unchanged, and I still remember my dear ones, and with unaltered love I still watch my old home. And although I cannot go to

you, you can some day come to me. First you must finish your work on earth. Go back to your home in the Earth Country. You will become a great Chief among your people. Rule wisely and justly and well, and give freely of your food to the poor among the Indians who have not as much as you have. And when your work on earth is done you shall come to me in this Land of Shadows beyond the Country of Silence, and we shall be together again and our youth and strength and beauty will never leave us.'

And the boy, wondering greatly and in deep sorrow, said: 'Let me stay with you now.' But his sister said: 'That cannot be.' Then he said: 'I will give you a Shadow which you must keep with you as your guardian spirit. And while you have it with you, no harm can come to you, for it will be present only in the light, and where there is Light there can be no wickedness. But when it disappears you must be on your guard against doing evil, for then there will be darkness, and darkness may lead you wrong.'

So the boy took the Shadow and said goodbye for a season and set out on his homeward journey. The little white birds, which had waited for him in the trees, guided him back to the beach. His canoe was still there, but the skeleton-man had gone and there was not a trace of him to be found upon the sand. And the Island of the Blest was silent except for the songs of the birds and the ripple of the little streams. The boy embarked in his canoe and sailed towards the east, and as he pushed off from the beach the little white birds left him and disappeared in the air. The sea was now calm and there was no storm, as there had been on his outward journey. Soon he reached the shore on the other side. He left his canoe in the cove as the old man had told him, and in a few days he arrived at his home, still bearing the Shadow from the Country of Silence.

He worked hard for many years but he did no evil, and in the end he became a great Chief and did much good for his people. He ruled wisely and justly and well, as his sister had commanded him. Then one day, when he was old and his work was done, he disappeared, and his people knew that he had gone to join his sister in the Land of Shadows in the Country of Silence far away, somewhere in the west. But he left behind him the Shadow his sister had given him; and while there is Light, the Indians still have their Shadow and no harm can come to them, for where there is Light there can be no evil.

But always in the late autumn the Shadows of the Indian brother and sister in the Country of Silence are lonely for their former life. And they think of their living friends and of the places of their youth, and they wish once more to follow the hunt, for they know that the hunter's moon is shining. And when their memory dwells with longing on their earlier days, their spirits are allowed to come back to earth for a brief season from the Land of Shadows. Then the winds are silent and the days are very still, and the smoke of their camp-fires appears like haze upon the air. And men call this season Indian Summer, but it is really but a Shadow of the golden summer that has gone. And it always is a reminder to the Indians that in the Land of Shadows, far away in the Country of Silence in the west, there are no dead.